BASIC ONE BRAIN

DYSLEXIC LEARNING CORRECTION AND BRAIN INTEGRATION

by
Gordon Stokes/Daniel Whiteside

Published by
THOTH, INC
2533 N. Carson St., Suite 751
Carson City, NV 89706

ISBN 0-918993-00-8

Third Edition 1992

Library of congress Catalog Card Number: 86-50215

ISBN 0-918993-00-8

SPECIAL NOTE

The procedures and techniques described in this manual are solely for information purposes. The Authors and Three In One Concepts are not directly or indirectly presenting any part of this work as a diagnosis or prescription for any ailment of any reader, or even recommend these natural procedures, or make representation concerning the physiological effects for any of the ideas reported. Persons using the tests and correction procedures reported here do so entirely at their own risk.

ACKNOWLEDGEMENTS

While the ONE BRAIN <u>system</u> developed from our independent thought, its roots go deep into discoveries and disciplines from many sources - including what we've learned from our work with clients and the students in our programs. "Out of the need comes more." You'll find specific technical sources listed in the text and bibliography. Still, we want to give special credit to Drs. George Goodheart, John Thie and Sheldon Deal for their creative work in the development of Applied Kinesiology, to Robert Shane for his part in brainstorming ONE BRAIN's over-all schema, to Rick Utt for the Clear Circuit concept, and to the three of us at Three In One for our energy, intuition and willingness to step out of the main stream to help others <u>know</u> they KNOW.

TABLE OF CONTENTS

CHAPTER 9
STEP BY STEP RUN THROUGH

APPENDIX
SUMMARY
SCHEMA
CHECK LIST

INDEX

THE PROBLEM: HOW TO IDENTIFY AND DEFUSE THE DYSLEXIAS THAT CREATE LEARNING DYSFUNCTIONS

In the mid-1960's, the medical establishment regarded the newly-diagnosed conditions called "dyslexia" and "dyslexic learning dysfunctions" as the result of lesions in the brain. Children who couldn't read or write adequately, or who transposed words, characters or symbols or went "blind" to whole phrases were written off as brain damaged, and the only treatment offered consisted of medication for those cases which also involved hyperactive behavior. For the next decade, anyone diagnosed as dyslexic faced a pretty bleak future.

In the 1970s, people with dyslexia took hope from new brain research that disclaimed the "lesion" theory in favor of "a failure to learn coordination during earliest childhood." Some pretty remarkable work began along the line of re-educating the brain/body in motor skills. With this increase of integrated function, many young students made stunning progress in their learning skills as well as their ability to handle their emotions.

In the early 1980s, researchers found a whole new theory to explain learning dysfunctions. They announced that the problem resulted from "a failure of the right and left brain hemispheres to integrate." Right Brain/Left Brain information achieved instant and enormous popularity. Now at last the enemy had been identified! LEFT BRAIN, the analytical learner of the two hemispheres, was at fault for busily blocking the sainted creativity of RIGHT BRAIN's wholistic vision. With "Develop the Right Brain!" as its watch-cry, a major movement began. Its answer to dyslexic learning dysfunctions focused on consciously directed Right Brain activity, cross-over coordination exercise and a positive, supportive environment in which to learn with the goal of integrating and equalizing the two brain hemispheres.

Today, the medical establishment continues to prescribe drugs like dramamine to rebalance the inner ear, thus eliminating the motion-sickness syndrome which IS rightly associated with dys-coordination difficulties. The Human Potential/Wholistic movement has, for the most part, embraced the integrated hemispheres approach. And just about everybody sees "significant progress" being made, using their method of choice.

Well, here comes an entirely different approach. ONE BRAIN makes a brand new case for what dyslexia IS, how it comes to exist, and how to correct its original cause.

Our source? Any current text on anatomy, physiology and/or neurology. The information has been available - and self-evident - since Arthur Guyton's PHYSIOLOGY OF THE HUMAN BODY and SPEECH AND BRAIN MECHANISMS by Wilder Penfield/Lamar Roberts were first published in 1959. Why the medical establishment and the Wholistic movement haven't put the obvious 2 + 2 together escapes us entirely, because the answer to the problem of dyslexia appears so simple once a person understands the basic functions of the brain itself.

WHAT IS "DYSLEXIA"?

Very infrequently, dyslexia results from an actual lesion (separation of tissue) in the brain which affects speech, language perception or comprehension. Occasionally, these negative effects relate to problems associated with the inner ear. Some of the time, mis-communication between the right/left brain hemispheres is a major factor. But in almost every instance, "learning dysfunctions" - popularly termed "dyslexia" - result from emotional stress at the time of learning, a stress so intense that the individual programs in a blind spot to a given learning skill due to fear, fear of pain or pain itself.

Except when caused by actual physical trauma to brain tissue, **dyslexia results from a denial that learning is possible in a specific area of life experience. This denial comes from a conscious CHOICE made in a moment of intense emotional stress.** It's a simple neurological function, not a "dysfunction" at all!

Nor does dyslexia lock a limitation on life. Even in the very rare instance where dyslexia has a clinical cause (physical trauma), the human mind can find its way around such perceptual blind spots. It's common knowledge that most dyslexics become amazingly creative when it comes to handling (not to mention masking) the "problem." In our experience, the MOST creative people have dyslexia, know it, and put their creative focus on areas of expression which aren't affected by that particular blind spot.

Certainly dyslexia hasn't blocked the creative writing of a Stephen J. Cannell, or the performance potential of a Cher, both of whom are more than willing to talk about their dyslexia. They recognize the problem and have made a direct attack on doing something about it - which is, obviously, the very best thing to do.

However, most dyslexics never bother to identify "what's wrong." Instead, they content themselves with the knowledge that "I just don't read well, so I don't read very much" - or "I'm no good at handwriting, so I use the typewriter" - or "I never could do math, so I have someone else post the figures. That's what accountants are for, isn't it?"

Of course, such denial does nothing to correct the situation. In fact, denying one problem is a CHOICE that sets the pattern for denying ALL problems. Still, most people would rather make do with a limitation rather than publicly admit there's something wrong in order to get the help they need - which is just plain silly, when you stop to think that (in a neurological system as wonderful as ours) no condition of limitation need ever become a dead end. What dead-ends us is the emotional stress we attach to having "an identified problem."

The truth is that we ALL have dyslexic learning dysfunctions. It doesn't matter how well we read, comprehend, write or do math. Somewhere along the way of growing up, we hit a brick wall of overwhelming emotional stress and CHOSE to go blind to some area of learning. What's more, from then on, we denied the possibility we could ever master that subject. This CHOICE TO DENY our capability condemned us to daily cover our tracks lest anyone discover we were less than our best. And to compound the problem, our CHOICE TO DENY took place so long ago, most of us "can't remember" when or why that CHOICE was made! Having forgotten (or, more accurately <u>suppressed</u> the memory of) such causal events, we feel helpless to change their effects in present time.

THE BOTTOM LINE ON DYSLEXIA is the fear, pain or fear of pain which made us check out "THEN" and the Belief System which maintains the condition as an integral part of self-image "NOW."

THE ONE BRAIN SYSTEM DEFUSES DYSLEXIC FUSION

An emotionally-caused blockage in perception is like the process of **fusion** - the melting together of two elements <u>under great heat</u> which causes them to lose much of their individual nature. In "the heat of intense emotion" - specifically fear, pain or fear of pain - we <u>fused</u> our ability to perceive with our inability to "survive" in the situation, and <u>chose to go blind to the causor rather than deal with</u> any <u>more pain.</u> Since this **fusion** happened prior to the present, it's necessary to find a way to alert the memory neurons which "were firing" at that moment and **defuse** the Negative Emotional Charge they maintain.

Without defusion of <u>past</u> causors, no present-time correction lasts longer than the next similar stressor.

The ONE BRAIN system deals directly with both present AND past in order to free the future from the **Negative Emotional Charge** that blocks perception. We identify the exact nature of the <u>blockage</u> as it exists in present time. This automatically keys-in all related memory patterns from the past. **Age Recession** then identifies where on the time-track we <u>fused</u> Negative Emotional Charge to the issue of perception.

THE NEUROLOGICAL MODUS OPERANDI OF DYSLEXIA

Once again, dyslexia could result from damage to brain tissue or pathology of the inner ear or (and far more often) some form of mis-communication between brain hemispheres. But almost always, the problem exists because of a mis-communication between the fore and backbrain portions of the Dominant Brain Hemisphere only. Responding to Negative Emotional Charge, the Dominant Hemisphere shuts down its full, balanced function in favor of physical/emotional survival, which results in minimal brain function.

The modus operandi of dyslexia is found in the Common Integrative Area of the Dominant Hemisphere which has the power to deny both its own forebrain functions AND the function of the Alternate Brain. And since this check-out process can take place only in the Dominant Brain Hemisphere, it's logical to conclude that dyslexic blind spots are created and maintained in that hemisphere.

Understanding HOW the "brains" work (individually and as ONE BRAIN) makes for more assurance when it comes to defusing the Negative Emotional Charge that locks-in dyslexia. For this reason we want to review the basics of brain function before we talk about anything else.

THE DOMINANT BRAIN HEMISPHERE

Generally speaking, the Dominant Hemisphere is the <u>left</u> brain hemisphere. But not always, hence our use of the term "Dominant" versus "Left." (Nine times out of ten, the Dominant hemisphere is opposite the hand you write with.) It's characterized by two unique capabilities: Speech/Language and the Common Integrative Area (the center of the self-oriented Belief System). Primarily, Dominant's forebrain half has to do with right now/present time <u>awareness,</u> while the backbrain portion houses the long-term memories which prompt our usual physical/emotional reactions as based on past experience.

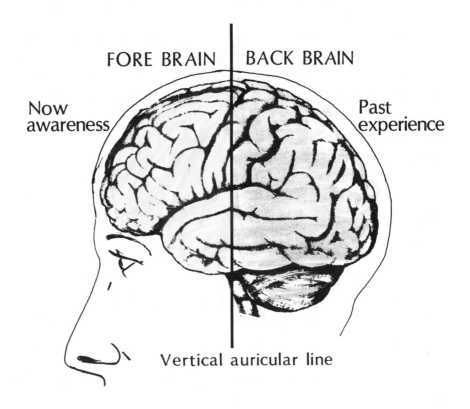

FORE BRAIN | BACK BRAIN

Now awareness

Past experience

Vertical auricular line

nomenclature, the fore and back brains are
he Vertical Auricular Line, a not-so-arbitrary
landmark which takes the form of a line vertical to the
orifice of the ear. ("Auricular" means "of or pertaining to
the EAR".)

But before going into detail about the job descriptions of
fore/back brains, it's important to underscore two
neurological basics:

The furthest extension of the nervous system
CAN control the <u>entire</u> nervous system
and
The brain functions on an <u>all or nothing</u> basis

The "furthest extension" refers to that part of the cerebral
cortex known as the Conscious Associational Thinking area
(hereafter: <u>CAT</u>). We find CAT in the frontal lobes of both
hemispheres. It represents the most significant DIFFERENCE
of <u>CELL PROPORTION</u> between human and all other
mammalian brains. Only human beings have such a
proportional MASS of cells in this brain area. Such being the
case, you'd think that our behavior would be
CHARACTERIZED by its unique function, especially when you
know what CAT can do when "in charge" of brain activity.

CAT has the <u>power to inhibit</u> every "lower" neurological
activity including backbrain functions, physical motion - even
heartbeat and breathing. There's NO function of the body
which can't be consciously controlled <u>when this area of the
brain is "in charge."</u> Unfortunately it's in charge less than
5% of the time in most adults. **At least 95% of the time,
CONTROL centers in the <u>Dominant</u> Hemisphere's
Common Integrative Area (hereafter: <u>CIA</u>).**

Why? Underlined: Emotional stress.

Under stress, Dominant's CIA takes total charge, withdrawing circulation from all brain areas not directly related to physical/emotional survival. This leaves CAT out in the cold and guarantees the duplication of past reaction patterns - most of which leave much to be desired. Since we're in some degree of stress MOST of the time, the frightening reality is that we use less than one quarter of our brain potential AS THE RULE - 95% of the time.

More on stress later; for now we wanted you to realize that when you look at the illustration of Dominant Brain its functions appear balanced in terms of forebrain/backbrain cell proportion. Actually, it doesn't work that way at all - unless we actively assist it. Instead, **CAT**'s power of new options takes a continual back seat to **CIA**'s conditioned Belief System.

Since this is the hard (very hard!) reality, let's take a look at backbrain's function first.

DOMINANT BACKBRAIN

Everything behind the Vertical Auricular Line (hereafter: VAL) concerns itself with memory, the process of current sensation, and muscle activity reactive to sensation. EMOTION is a sensation, and intensity of emotion in the moment determines the impact of any given experience on memory. Basically, emotion lives in Dominant's TEMPORAL lobe, while the memory of emotion houses itself throughout the other lobes in locations appropriate to the sensations and activities involved.

Dominant's OCCIPITAL lobe is the primary process center for what's perceived by the physical eye and "the mind's eye," accepting what both perceive as real and of equal priority.

Dominant's PARIETAL lobe centers the awareness coming from/through the body, hence the descriptive "somesthetic" label ("somesthetic" means "sensations from the body"). Significant large muscle activity is triggered in the parietal lobe and adjacent portions of the frontal lobe.

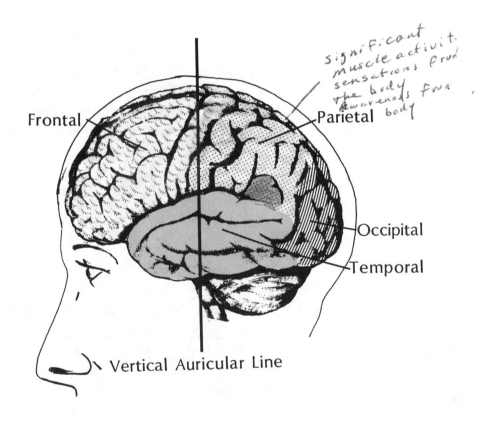

Frontal

Parietal

Occipital

Temporal

Vertical Auricular Line

significant muscle activit. sensations from the body awareness from body

The small part of the FRONTAL which extends behind VAL had to do with muscular activation of the feet, legs, trunk and shoulders.

THE COMMON INTEGRATIVE AREA

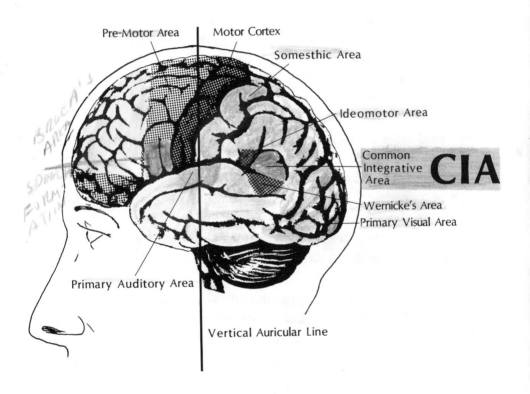

Located between the three major sensation-processing areas - visual, auditory and somesthetic (sensations from the body) - the **CIA** occupies a prominent position on the posterior surface of Dominant's temporal (intense emotion) lobe. In addition to visual, auditory and somesthetic input, the CIA also receives signals directly from the thalamus and other basal areas of the brain. Its job is to automatically connect remembered experience with current sensation to determine a common meaning (which is the reason for its name, COMMON INTEGRATIVE AREA). And once it has established a common meaning, CIA selects the "best way" to react, based on previous survival patterns.

For example: let's say that someone happened to be at home and heard an electrical pop, saw the lights dim, and smelled smoke, that person might not be able to tell from any ONE of these sensations exactly what had taken place, but from all of them together could readily assess the danger. The CIA correlates the totality of sense input and weighs one against the other to reach deeper conclusions than can be reached by any of the sense association areas alone.

Once the CIA reaches its conclusion, it sends signals into other portions of the brain to cause appropriate responses. Most of the signals pass to an area immediately anterior to the CIA called the IDEOMOTOR AREA. This is closely associated with the CIA, for it selects the muscular activity appropriate to CIA's command. To put it another way, the Ideomotor Area translates the idea (or image or emotion) into action (muscular response). Quite naturally, it's always found on CIA's side of the brain, and yet it controls muscular activity on both sides of the body simultaneously.

The CIA is our self-image center, the center of "ego" (which means, literally, "I AM") and therefore the housing of our Belief System and self-esteem as well. In effect, it's the "I AM (fill-in-the-blank)" headquarters computer - and as with all computers, the rule of GIGO applies (GIGO stands for Garbage In/Garbage Out in computer parlance). What we believe to be true is the ROM of the CIA computer. Whether that "truth" is valid, profitable, or self-destructive makes no difference because, of itself, the CIA has no choice except to duplicate all past experience relevant to the immediate survival of the personality as it has come to believe itself to be.

THE NATURE OF CIA-BASED MEMORY is highly selective. It presents the information a person wants to believe, and suppresses those memories the person finds painful. This takes place in the same manner a film editor puts a movie together - in bits and pieces, re-shaping "the reality" to conform with a preconceived design. Dominant Brain's remembrance is like an edited half-hour version of GONE WITH THE WIND - shot through with blanks, blindspots and assumptions - cut to fit the Belief System's image of "reality."

No wonder Dominant has to function analytically, straining to focus down on specifics to "understand" them based on past programming. And no wonder Dominant is judgmental! It reflects all the conditioned "dyslexias" involved in the life-learning process. And what emotions etch in those dyslexias? FEAR, PAIN and FEAR OF PAIN, of course. Which means that Dominant's primary motivators are negative emotional states which of their very nature limit - and, more often than not, defeat - the desire for positive, profitable self-improvement.

Not that it "has to be" that way.

CIA knows the positives, too - all the positive wins, the wonders, we've created. But CIA's <u>priority</u> is SURVIVAL, whatever will keep us from suffering FEAR, PAIN or FEAR OF PAIN. Hence (and alas!) **CIA views CHANGE as HARM.** Thus it does its best to block changes which would re-arrange its Belief System - even if such changes would benefit us!

THE SPEECH/LANGUAGE CENTERS

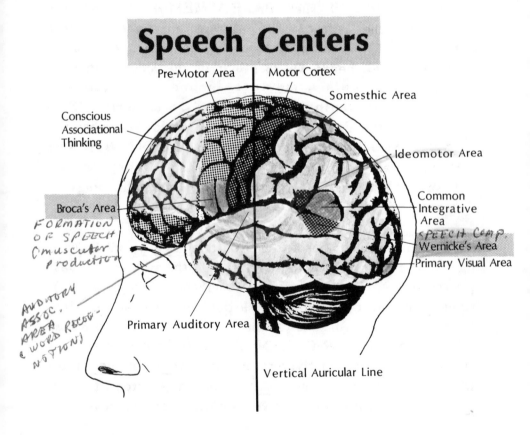

Dominant Brain's other unique function, SPEECH/LANGUAGE, finds dual housing facilities available - with speech comprehension centered in WERNICKE's area of the temporal lobe, geographically adjacent to the CIA, which suggests we comprehend according to how we FEEL about what we hear. The formation of speech, however, lives in BROCA's area of the frontal lobe, below CAT - which suggests that we can speak "clear" of CIA's emotional programming, at least to some extent, when we're not under stress.

Clinically speaking, a lesion (separation or ulceration of tissue) in either Broca's speech area or Wernicke's speech area leads to a disruption of speech, but the symptoms of the two disorders differ. These differences reflect the nature of the lobes of the brain on which they're located.

Broca's speech center is in Dominant Brain's frontal lobe, near CAT, and controls the muscular production of speech. If this area receives pathological damage, the person's speech becomes labored and slow with impaired articulation. Response to questions often makes sense, but generally the answers aren't expressed in fully formed or grammatical sentences. Example, a patient asked about a dental appointment said hesitantly and indistinctly: "Yes. . . Monday. . . Dad and Dick. . . Wednesday nine o'clock. . . 10 o'clock. . . doctors. . . and teeth." The same kinds of errors appear in the person's writing as well.

On the other hand, Wernicke's area is located on the temporal lobe with a direct relationship to the CIA. It handles speech comprehension. If this area suffers damage, a person's speech is phonetic and even grammatically normal, but words string together in haphazard fashion. Asked to describe a picture that showed two boys stealing cookies behind a woman's back, one such sufferer responded: "Mother is away here working her work to get her better, but when she's looking the two boys, taking in the other part. She's working another time."

Wernicke's area also takes a major role in the written word and "heard" words, as well. No surprise there; after all, to see a word is to pronounce it mentally, just as hearing a word we see and feel it, too (as colored by our emotional experience and Belief System). The same applies to the hands-on writing of words. Neurologically, when we hear a word, the sound-signal goes first to the primary auditory cortex but must pass through the adjacent Wernicke's area to be understood as a verbal message. When we read a word, its visual pattern is first perceived by the primary visual cortex, then transmitted to the CIA which compounds it instantly with its auditory form in Wernicke's area.

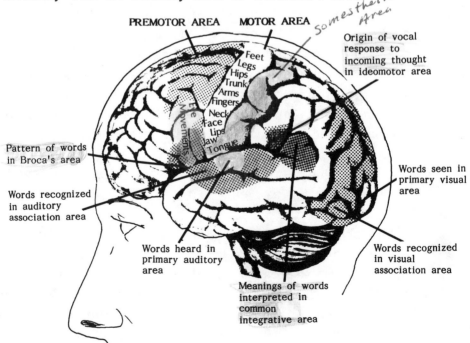

PREMOTOR AREA   MOTOR AREA   Somesthetic Area

Origin of vocal response to incoming thought in ideomotor area

Feet
Legs
Hips
Trunk
Arms
Fingers
Neck
Face
Lips
Jaw
Tongue

Eye Movements

Pattern of words in Broca's area

Words recognized in auditory association area

Words heard in primary auditory area

Words seen in primary visual area

Words recognized in visual association area

Meanings of words interpreted in common integrative area

Do you begin to shudder at the infinite opportunities for trauma-charged short-circuits, the multiples of blind-spots that can occur in the above processes?

And they're just small potatoes compared with what's involved with hand-writing. No wonder so many people hate to even sign their names! Think of the incredible number of steps in that process. Not only does the image of the word as you WANT it to appear have its separate perception, but so does the word you see as you write it. Then there's the processing of all the muscular activities involved to be interrelated with the mental sounding of the word, the seeing of the word, the feeling of the word, the body sensations attached to what that word means in your Belief System, the memories of how you felt learning to form the letters which make up the word - and that's just the tip of the iceberg.

Let's face it. The number of people suffering from pathological damage to Broca's or Wernicke's area is infinitesimal in terms of the general population's mass dyslexic dysfunction. But SOMETHING causes people to speak indistinctly (Brocan trauma), or spew forth inappropriate gobbledegook (Wernickian trauma), and that something is trauma, all right - EMOTIONAL TRAUMA.

Keep in mind that we don't create a Dominant Hemisphere until we learn how to speak. Prior to that, both hemispheres function as equals, each doing its own work in supporting the other as appropriate to the needs of the moment. With the acquisition of LANGUAGE comes the awareness of comparatives, goods/bads, shoulds and should nots, I am/I am not, rewards/punishments, etc. Language brings definitions; definitions bring limitation. Language puts the emphasis on sense experience and, in doing so, of its very nature denies multi-dimensional perception. It also saddles us with categories instead of conception, pigeon-holes rather than perception.

DOMINANT FOREBRAIN

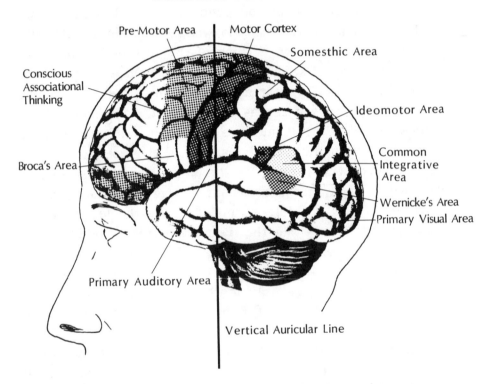

As you can see in the illustration, the forebrain (anterior to VAL) consists primarily of the frontal lobe, with some of the temporal and very little of the parietal lobe included. Muscular activation of face, lips, jaw and tongue takes place anterior to VAL (parietal/frontal). But the frontal lobe's primary cell proportion devoted to muscular activation is the Pre-Motor area, and its job is <u>eye movement only</u>.

Understand that the comparative proportion of cells devoted to a given brain function determines the IMPORTANCE of that function to the inherent NATURE of the life <u>form</u>.

For instance, for creatures who survive by their sense of smell, the olfactory lobes of the brain are commensurately large; in humans they're almost negligible in terms of overall brain proportion. Another example: the primary visual area in marmosets is enormous, compared with the same proportion in humans - and marmosets, structurally, are "all eyes" when you look at them. Bottom line: the comparative size of an exterior sense organ indicates the basic emphasis of brain proportion for that creature.

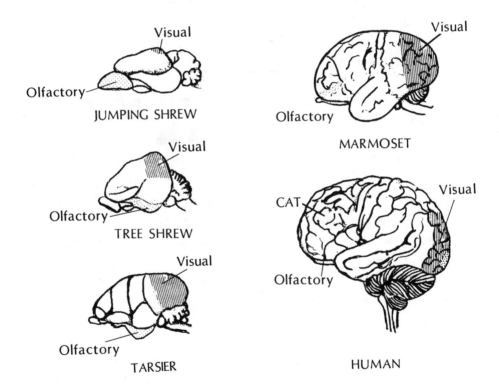

Since we humans have so great a brain proportion devoted to eye movements, it's little wonder that "how we see what we see" is germane to comprehension. If there's a mis-communication (read: "short-circuit") between our visual process and the visual memory bank (backbrain), we function inefficiently (read: "dyslexic").

A NOTE ON HOW WE SEE

If your head could be completely immobilized and your eye movements cease altogether, everything around you would become a blur and you'd see nothing. What causes the eyes to function is STIMULATION, and movement provides this stimulation.

Vision depends on impulses transferred along the optic nerve to visual analyzer cells located in the Primary Visual Area of the occipital backbrain. Surrounding these cells are visual association cells, which organize what is seen into meaningful visual patterns. As the final step in this hierarchy, a third group of cells surrounds the first two. This third group has the responsibility for coordinating both what we see and what we hear into a single perception. Should trauma interrupt this process, the system short-circuits, creating a "blind-spot" toward what is being seen. Reinforced by repetition, this blind-spot becomes dyslexic visual perception.

The forebrain's temporal lobe activity also includes the Primary Auditory Area, and the primary auditory memory-bank. The symbolic significance of Auditory's location offers much to the imagination, suggesting that what we hear relates more to what we think, while what we SEE relates more to what we FEEL. ("I can't hear myself think," is the classic statement along that line.)

The formation of speech center (BROCA's area) lives in the frontal lobe, as mentioned earlier. We mention it again here to underscore the symbolic significance of its location. We have two kinds of verbal activity available as human beings: knee-jerk emotional reaction or consciously considered response. One is thought-less backbrain repetition of past tapes; the other speaks to NOW in thought-full expression.

The lower, basal, portion of the frontal lobe has a commonality with the brains of "lower" mammalian forms, but the cell proportion mid-way between the Pre-Motor and basal areas characterizes the human structure exclusively. This comparatively huge forebrain proportion houses our uniqueness as human beings.

THE CONSCIOUS ASSOCIATIONAL THINKING (**CAT**) AREA

CAT is to the forebrain what the CIA is to backbrain - the essence of its character and function. This is where new options, new alternatives, new anything takes place. And, along with this truly NOW awareness, CAT has short-term memory.

Why "short-term"? Because CAT-memories relate to first-time, or one-time-only perception. In order for such perception to register in the backbrain memory banks, it must be consciously repeated many times, or it must involve such intensity of emotion that a single experience engraves an indelible record.

Brain-mappers have a clear read-out in specific detail of every brain cell proportion except for CAT. Yet while the above general functions have been established for this MAJOR brain proportion, when artificially stimulated in test situations, CAT registers a single specific response: LIGHT - only light.

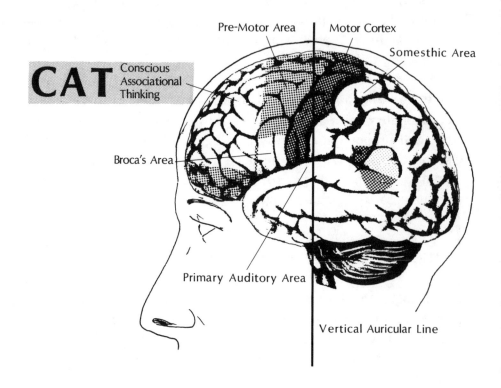

No wonder we have expressions such as "the light just went on," or "now I see the light!" That's exactly what happens when CAT has priority in our mental process - we see "the light" and, "in the light" of that perception, everything else can change. More important: this part of the brain has the power to INHIBIT any other function of the brain or body. As neurologists agree: "the furthest extension of the nervous system controls the nervous system." CAT is that "furthest extension."

Using CAT, we can do just about anything because CAT HAS NO FEELING/EMOTION ATTACHED TO ITS FUNCTION. That's right: no emotion. When CAT's operating as the primary influence, all past and/or current feeling/emotion seems "fuzzy" to us - relatively unimportant. We're just right there, in present time, experiencing AS IS.

What's more, like the alternate hemisphere CAT has no sense of time, limitation or judgment. Obviously, we'd all function as marvels were we to employ CAT as the brain area of choice. Alas, we go forebrain an infinitesimal amount of time, except for the act of speech (the speech ACTIVATING center is also part of the forebrain just below the Pre-Motor Area.) CAT - which contains our power to inhibit, to change, to CONSCIOUSLY choose - is short-circuited by emotional stress.

When stress is present in the system, when the stress hormones pump through our bodies, CAT simply doesn't "get through." We're in the mere-survival mode and functioning out of backbrain only. In effect, stress is a self-inflicted lobotomy, cutting us off from now awareness, options, alternatives and the power to self-direct.

To pound the final nail in the coffin of self-determination, keep in mind that CAT predominates in consciousness less than 5% of the time - when we could be using it 100% of the time. Just think what life would be like for us if we had a clear connection into Dominant's CAT most of the time? Everything would be different, and that difference would be NO NEGATIVE EMOTION since CAT automatically defuses CIA's impact and permits a CALM, emotion-free scan of what's going on with an eye to new options and alternatives.

SO HOW DO WE GET **CAT** IN GEAR?

The process of rebalancing fore/backbrain activity has one ground rule only. In order to activate the furthest extension of the nervous system we need to CHOOSE TO CHOOSE. This is not a metaphysical statement, it's a neurological reality. To bypass CIA dominance, we must CHOOSE TO CHOOSE. Only when we make that CHOICE does neuro-dominance shift from the CIA to CAT. Otherwise CIA dominates all mental processing.

We always have the power to make that choice - whenever we think of it. What's even more remarkable is how SELDOM we "think" to do it! And under stress we forget our power completely.

ONE BRAIN's emotional stress defusion skills assist a person to regain that power. **In fact, our whole purpose in ONE BRAIN is to give people back the power to re-integrate Dominant's fore and backbrains so that truly CONSCIOUS CHOICES can be made, CHOICES that change the PAST in order to create the kind of future the person really WANTS to have.**

That's the joy of this work, to see another human being regain the power of CHOICE, and watch positive changes come flowing forth - not just in so-called "learning dysfunctions," but in every area of life. And that's exactly what takes place when we defuse PAST stressors which blind us to what we really can achieve.

CHOOSE TO CHOOSE is Dominant Brain's computer-command to function AS A WHOLE. With CAT in gear, "the furthest extension of the nervous system" assumes command, negative emotion ceases to affect the conscious thought process and the door to options OPENS. What's more: when CAT's in command, the Alternate Brain's message comes more clearly into consciousness.

Which leads us into a brief review of basic information about:

DOMINANT/ALTERNATE BRAIN FUNCTION

Interconnected by the corpus callosum - an intricate bundle of nerve fibers - the two brain hemispheres form the wholeness of human individuality. Just remember, however, that at birth, neither hemisphere has dominance. Instead they work as equals to smooth the perception and response to life. The illustration below sums up the accepted model for the individual functions of Dominant and Alternate brains as they emerge in early childhood.

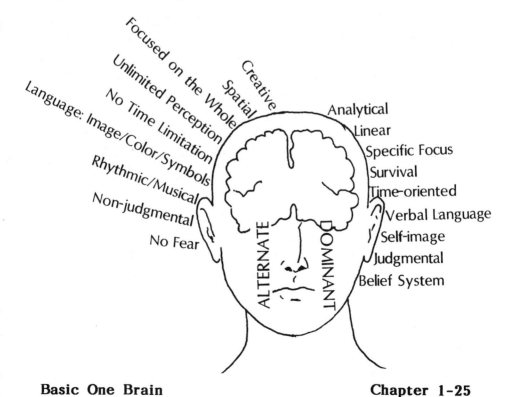

In infancy, a complex system of switches develops the ability to synchronize and integrate information so that the two hemispheres can work together in harmony and coordination. Memories are stored in duplicate; the massive communication system of the corpus callosum automatically lays down identical memory patterns in both hemispheres even in unusual situations which require the services of only one half of the brain. This carbon-copying of memory from one hemisphere to the other takes place only at the EXACT time an act or experience takes place.

One hemisphere can take over for the other, and can also operate on its own side to process tasks requiring no conscious control. For example: when we activate the language centers in the dominant brain in order to speak, the alternate hemisphere takes care of the gestures we make.

In general, the more complex or unfamiliar the task, the more both sides of the brain need to be involved in the operation until this material becomes more familiar and is taken over by the left hemisphere. EXAMPLE: Musically inexperienced listeners, recognize melodies better with their left ear (right hemisphere), while most concert-level musicians demonstrate a distinct right-ear (left hemisphere) advantage.

After brain dominance has been established, the hemispheres' equality vanishes. The DOMINANT (usually LEFT) hemisphere assumes its CIA characteristics with the result that it is taken up with details and, when damaged (or short-circuited), leaves the person capable of only sketchy and incomplete verbal and written production. This hemisphere "turns on" whenever we need to process computer-like information that has structure and sequence.

In CIA's <u>effort</u> to understand specifics, Dominant Brain becomes analytical and "linear" in operation. Its focus on SPECIFICS keys-in to SURVIVAL. Naturally it's time-oriented, since there's such concern with <u>limitation</u> and avoidance of fear, pain and/or fear of pain. This avoidance-syndrome makes Dominant extremely judgmental. Its conditioned Belief System is the final arbiter in all decisions, and physical survival is its bottom line. It thinks, feels and expresses in terms of verbal language and, in the process, <u>denies</u> the reality of any other form of expression.

The ALTERNATE (usually RIGHT brain) has responsibility for our visual memory, orientation in space, artistic ability, rhythm, and body awareness. It "turns on" when we need to process information as a whole, simultaneously, rather than in linear fashion. Interestingly, it knows what pain, fear and fear of pain ARE but responds to them as categories, not emotions. Therefore, Alternate is non-judgmental, has no sense of time or limitation and (since it doesn't contain the primary speech centers) functions most clearly in silence or in concert with music. Its "language" comes in the form of color, imagery and symbols.

Re: ALTERNATE (usually RIGHT) function, Dr. Jerry Levy, noted brain researcher with the University of Chicago, says, "This hemisphere's perception is holistic and doesn't depend on breaking things down into their component parts. We recognize a face instantaneously, for instance and, with the exception of novelists, few people are skilled at verbally describing what someone "looks like." In line with this, patients with damaged (short-circuited) right hemispheres have a great difficulty recognizing faces; sometimes even their own, despite intact language power."

THE CROSS-OVER NEUROLOGICAL FLOW

The RIGHT brain hemisphere controls the left eye, the left ear and the contraction of muscles on the left side of the body. The LEFT brain hemisphere controls the right eye, the right ear and the contraction of muscles on the right side of the body. Vice versa for <u>muscles in their EXTENDED positions.</u>

Remember that newborns' brain hemispheres function in equality. Only when we learn to 1) speak, 2) write and 3) read, does the CIA establish itself and one hemisphere assume dominance. The Dominant hemisphere's neurological flow controls the opposite eye, hand, side of the face and body. The Alternate's flow controls the other eye, hand, side of face and body. However, the images perceived by BOTH eyes, divide and go to both hemispheres.

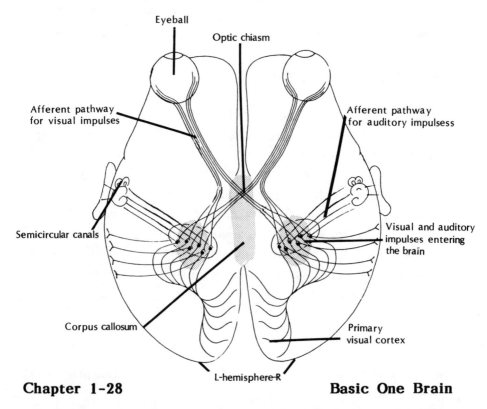

Eyeball

Optic chiasm

Afferent pathway for visual impulses

Afferent pathway for auditory impulsess

Semicircular canals

Visual and auditory impulses entering the brain

Corpus callosum

Primary visual cortex

L-hemisphere-R

This visual cross-over pattern is vital to innate, balanced function.

Alas, due to traumas such as physical accident and/or change-of-handedness at the time we learn to read and write, some of us find ourselves forced into an IPSILATERAL (same side) flow pattern - dominant right brain, eye, hand, etc. An ipsilateral flow of nerve messages puts the system into confusion and forces the two hemispheres to do double duty and becomes a major <u>unconscious</u> stressor to the system. Approximately 15% of the population quite likely has "mixed dominance" involved with any dyslexic dysfunction. Identifying and relieving this condition can be a very important step toward integrated brain function.

REVIEW: WHAT WE GAIN FROM THE ALTERNATE BRAIN

The Alternate is our "fair witness" - it's non-judgmental, NOT programmed by FEAR, and it has NO PRIMARY SPEECH CENTERS. Its language is IMAGE, RHYTHM, MELODY, HARMONY and COLOR.

Reinforce that awareness: Alternate Brain has NO speech centers similar to Dominant's. It "speaks an entirely different language" - and usually <u>in silence</u> or in rhythmic motion (dance), or humming/singing (music). And, since Alternate has no CIA, its memory is <u>complete</u>, UN-EDITED and <u>ALWAYS AVAILABLE.</u>

"The truth" of <u>any</u> memory is found in Alternate Brain's record, a record which notes everything AS IS and with NO <u>Belief System judgment.</u> That's what we mean by the term "fair witness." Alternate's memory IS what <u>really</u> happened, <u>not just how we FELT about it</u> (which characterizes the brand of memory CIA has to offer).

Alternate sees differently, too.

While Dominant's eye focuses down on specifics, Alternate sees THE WHOLE - which is why its memory is non-judgmental, in the Belief System sense. ALTERNATE sees/accepts/records the point of view of ALL PARTICIPANTS in a given experience. That's right; when recalling an incident via Alternate Brain, we're able to KNOW how the others involved were really feeling, too. How? Because we can see their expressions, body language, style and structure AS WAS. (Dominant/CIA memory sees only from OUR point of view. Consciously, we "overlook and disregard" the high signs of our antagonists. But alternate records it ALL!)

When you add the knowledge that Alternate INTEGRATES all body motion/muscular activity plus monitoring organic activity (such as heartbeat, breathing, etc.), you begin to APPRECIATE more fully THE WONDERS available to us when we consciously involve Alternate Brain function.

And all of those wonders become instantly available when Dominant CAT takes charge of brain function. This knowledge should inspire all of us to find ways to stay Dominant Forebrain as much as possible, especially under stress.

DYSLEXIA AND THE DOMINANT BRAIN

We're not making CIA the "bad guy," please understand. CIA has gotten us through the maze of surviving in a world of considerable suffering, fear and pain. Nor do we intend to make Dominant Brain the "bad guy" either. After all,

Dominant's CAT is ever available for <u>new options</u> and more! Plus, Dominant CAT has the power to scan CIA's "perception" - and <u>clear</u> it, too - if only we CHOOSE TO CHOOSE.

Yet, when stress overwhelmed us as little children, nobody told us how to handle it. We were never taught how our neurology worked and what to do to make it work better. How could we have know that emotional stress short-circuited the system - limiting our conscious brain function to the back half of the dominant brain hemisphere only? If only we'd known that **backbrain "survival"** can be whole brain suicide, we could have done something about it.

Yes, because we didn't realize we had a CHOICE at the time, we allowed fear, pain and/or fear of pain to <u>deny</u> us the freedom to be ourselves. CIA's emotionally-charged <u>denials</u> became the blindspots called "dyslexia."

What a waste, since - when the dominant hemisphere's CAT is the center of brain activity - the CIA stops re-hashing fear-based memory triggers and begins to pump out all the positives from past experience. That's right, once we go forebrain-dominant, we operate WITHOUT THE FEAR-BASED LIMITATIONS OF PAST FEELING/EXPERIENCE and we "get the good" of THE POSITIVE, SUCCESSFUL, PRODUCTIVE EXPERIENCE STORED <u>IN THE MEMORY BANKS OF BOTH BRAIN HEMISPHERES.</u> Forebrain pre-eminence permits alternate brain hemisphere equality. As Shakespeare says in Hamlet, "'tis a consummation devoutly to be wished."

An image to sum up the discussion: the CIA - which determines our usual reaction to anything - is approximately the size of a dime. That's why we say that our job at Three In One Concepts consists of helping people "get off the dime."

Well, that's the bad news about how dyslexia comes to consciousness. The good news is that these stress-related emotional traumas can be defused. To defuse stress, however, we need to <u>recognize</u> we're in stress, <u>identify</u> its cause, and <u>acknowledge</u> exactly how it has affected us. These are the first and all-important steps toward dyslexic defusion. Once we know we have a problem, once we <u>identify</u> it, we're half-way to the solution.

STRESS EQUALS DIMINISHED MENTAL CAPACITY

Here's the process by which conscious (and/or subconscious) stress leads to diminished capacity. When confronted by a challenge to our physical, mental, emotional or spiritual well-being, the body releases stress hormones into the bloodstream. These chemicals constrict the exterior capillaries of our vascular system, centering the blood supply in the thorax and in the long muscles of the body which would be involved in "fight or flight."

The same basic process takes place in the brain as well as in the body. The exterior capillaries constrict, centering the blood supply in the portions of the brain which have to do with physical survival. That feeling of "numbness" we have when in shock or physical stress means that the body has desensitized itself in order to survive. Unfortunately, with that desensitization comes the inability to think clearly - forebrain/CAT activity goes to functional zero and the backbrain/CIA rules!

We humans make the big mistake of believing we're in conscious control simply because we're still conscious. Not so; under stress we're into knee-jerk duplication of learned reactions based on negative emotion. If some of those learned reactions are dyslexic, then under stress our limitations increase drastically. (Just "try harder" to read when stressed and see how well you function!) The worst way to handle stressors is to deny they exist and/or that they're affecting our mental acuity. To deny a stressor's **Negative Emotional Charge** multiplies its power.

THE SIGNS OF STRESS

Fortunately we can recognize the body's stages of present stress at sight. All you need is a mirror to take a reading on yourself, and simple observation lets you read another person. The eyes tell "all" (or at least <u>enough</u> to clue us in that physical/mental dominion is in short supply). Here's why.

FIRST STAGE STRESS

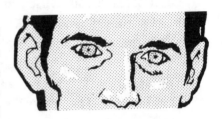

In a moment of shock (or when fatigue at last overwhelms us), the withdrawal of blood from the body's exterior means that the pores close, forcing out the oil they contain. Also, the tear-ducts close, denying moisture to the eye. The over-all effect is a dry, staring pair of eyes and shiny skin. A little later - when exposure to air evaporates the oil/moisture - the skin's "shiny" look disappears and the eyes become dull, their lids drooping to protect the eyeballs' drier surface. In such a state, our mind is as dull as our eyes and our mental acuity is functionally nil. The lights aren't on and nobody's home.

SECOND STAGE STRESS

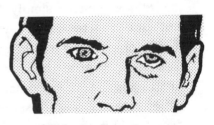

As stress continues unrelieved for hours at a time, depth perception is affected. Owing to our maternal/paternal genetic make-up, one side of our body has a more sensitive structure than the other, due to the difference of the maternal/paternal genetic contributions. This is particularly true of the extremely delicate muscles affixed to the eyeballs. As stress chemicalization remains in the body, the more sensitively structured eye muscles constrict and begin to rotate the eyeball upward. This limits depth perception temporarily since one eye now sees "off" its accustomed level and the brain has to re-train itself to perceive accurately. Until it does, our perception is "inaccurate" and we're subject to the kind of mishaps which a failure in depth perception produces. In fact, we become <u>accident prone</u>. (The technical term for this up/down off-level rotation is "vertical strabismus." For people with a tendency toward inward/outward muscular eyeball rotation, it's "lateral strabismus.") When you see more white (sclera) showing under one iris than the other, you're looking at Second Stage Stress.

NOTE: The eye that's off-level tells you a LOT about the nature of the stress a person's experiencing. If DOMINANT's eye has rotated upward, the person's "trying too hard" to force, or to control self or others in a current situation - and can't see the whole in relation to its parts. If ALTERNATE's eye has gone up, confusion in understanding the parts and "giving up" may characterize the person's attitude. Don't overlook the possibility that such "giving up" includes the denial of creative/artistic (read: "self-fulfilling") expression.

Don't assume right eye = Dominant and left = Alternate. Check handedness before reaching a conclusion.

THIRD STAGE STRESS
Should stress continue unresolved for days, weeks or longer, the other eye adjusts to match the upward rotation of the first and restore usual depth perception.

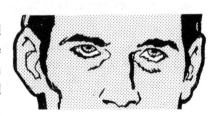

When white (sclera) shows under both irises, you're seeing a person with an unresolved, obsessive problem - physical, emotional, mental or spiritual in nature. There's some form of PAIN/FEAR he or she "doesn't want to look at," or won't acknowledge, OR "can't" do anything about. (Frequently this takes the form of seeing only <u>one</u> alternative, which in itself is unacceptable).

EMERGENCY ALERT
When you see a person whose <u>pupils</u> remain expanded or contracted regardless of changes in exterior light, you're looking at a person with one of the following conditions:

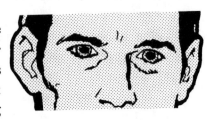

ADRENAL OVERWHELM, in which the body has exhausted its supply of adrenalin. More: whether expanded or contracted, the pupil constantly fluctuates. Also, people in Adrenal Overwhelm have an allergenic reaction to natural fruit sugars and a positive response to refined sugar - a complete reverse of the usual situation. When you see this sign of stress, suggest the person have a physical check-up, with emphasis on the adrenal system.

RESPONSE TO MEDICATION, a temporary pathology caused by an allergenic response.

HABITUAL CONSCIOUS CHOICE, either <u>to limit</u> (contracted pupil) the amount of light/emotion perceived or expressed by the eye, or <u>to open</u> self emotionally (expanded pupil) to the light within.

SO, TO REVIEW THE SIGNS OF STRESS:

FIRST STAGE: Immediate or recent stress = glazed eye.

SECOND STAGE: Continued stress = temporary strabismus in one eye.

THIRD STAGE: Prolonged stress/unresolved problem = temporary strabismus of both eyes.

EMERGENCY ALERT: Abnormal and extended contraction or expansion of the pupils of the eyes.

Take a careful look at the physical indicators of these states and degrees of visible stress as shown in the illustration. To recognize them in others can prove invaluable; being willing to recognize them in yourself may be the first step toward releasing their negative causors - one of which is undoubtedly some form of dyslexia (given our up-front broad definition).

THE SIGNS OF STRESS

FIRST STAGE STRESS

Staring eyes, shiny skin

SECOND STAGE STRESS

White showing under one eye

THIRD STAGE STRESS

White showing under both eyes

EMERGENCY ALERT

Enlarged pupil

HOW TO IDENTIFY DYSLEXIC DYSFUNCTION
AND ITS CAUSE

The traditional way to elicit information takes the form of an interview in which questions and answers provide clues that result in a trial and error effort to understand a given condition or reach an agreement. Even if all parties concerned desire a completely honest verbal exchange, too many unknowns can influence the outcome of the interview approach. That's because current CONSCIOUSNESS represents only the sum-total of what we believe to be true about ourselves based on past conditioning - which is very likely riddled with emotional blindspots and life lies.

And as to the SUBCONSCIOUS - well, we wouldn't trust the negative aspects of SUBCONSCIOUSNESS any further than we could throw them (if only we had that right)! Our experience has been that both CONSCIOUS and SUBCONSCIOUS have too many editorial blank-outs to be trusted for genuine self-evaluation. Plus, the Q & A process is of itself a major stressor; it puts us on the spot. So when we use direct questions, the answers we receive all too likely come from less than one-quarter of the answerer's brain.

So if we can't trust conscious or subconscious memory to cough up the complete and honest truth, to whom can we apply for that most prized of all commodities? Who-or-what-else knows and can/will reveal the bottom line?

The body - through Clear Circuit Muscle Testing.

With Clear Circuit testing, both brain hemispheres have the opportunity to respond as equals to a given test or question. In this way, we can receive both Dominant's Belief System response AND Alternate's fair-witness input on ANY issue that affects an individual's physical and/or emotional well-being.

Also, a muscle test alerts more of our brain cells than does mental evaluation. Its extra muscular activity <u>and sense input</u> expands both the amount and quality of information reaching the brain. During the test, the brain gets feedback in its own language, <u>kinesthetic perception</u>, beyond any it could receive through conscious deliberation.

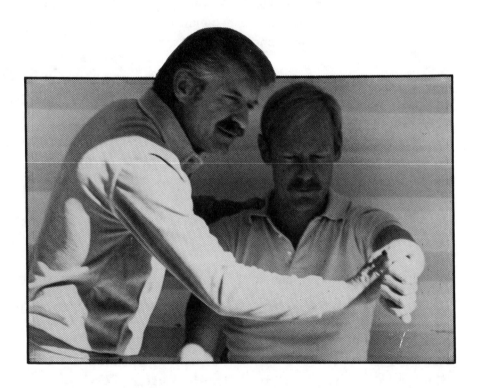

If you're new to the concept of muscle-testing as a means of receiving feedback from the body, the technique may seem unusual to say the least. Yet, for the last ten years, our experience has borne out its accuracy under all kinds of test conditions. In fact, all of our work at Three In One Concepts is predicated on that accuracy. For this reason, when it comes to identifying the dyslexias associated with learning dysfunctions - AND when it comes to verifying that such neurological blockages have been defused - our procedure of choice is the Clear Circuit Muscle Test.

BACKGROUND BASICS

Muscle testing per se originated in Applied Kinesiology as a way to determine whether a given muscle group functioned normally. To verify that normal state, AK researchers positioned a muscle in its <u>contracted state</u> and applied pressure to move the muscle toward its <u>extended state</u>. If the muscle "held strong," it functioned normally. If it "went weak" when tested, this indicator CHANGE meant the muscle was "under-energy."

To rebalance such under-energy, AK uses acupressure massage, manipulation of muscles' proprioceptors, and other techniques. The result: increased coordination, release of muscular stress, postural improvement, cessation of pain and spasm, as well as many other physical positives. In addition, AK developed the concept that muscle testing could determine the effect of emotional as well as physical trauma on the body. To relieve the effect of such emotional trauma, AK uses holding key neurovascular points (the frontal eminences/CAT).

Deservedly, AK has received general and enthusiastic acceptance within the field of Wholistic Health and is achieving more and more recognition within the medical establishment. How could it be otherwise when the results of AK muscle-testing has a track record of 80% accuracy?

At Three In One Concepts, we've refined the AK muscle testing model even more in our effort to increase the accuracy of test results. **Clear Circuit Testing of indicator muscles in both contraction AND extension on BOTH sides of the body/brain insures the greatest accuracy possible.**

MUSCLE TESTING: FEEDBACK FROM THE BODY

DEFINITION

A Muscle Test is the application of slow, gentle, light pressure to a given muscle in either its contracted or extended position.

If you're brand new to muscle testing, one picture's worth a thousand words. Please take a look at the accompanying illustrations. It shows the person's Anterior Deltoid being tested in two positions - contraction and extension. You'll use both positions during ONE BRAIN testing procedures. Why? Because the contracted position on each side is 80% controlled by its appropriate brain hemisphere and 20% by the other brain. Vice versa, with the muscle positioned in extension. By testing BOTH RIGHT AND LEFT LIMBS IN BOTH POSITIONS, you involve 100% of both brains. This will be important to verify that emotional defusion and/or physical correction have taken place and that the whole brain "agrees" with the result.

For purposes of illustration, "CONTRACTION" means that the muscle has been positioned at the peak of its forward/upward range of motion (before other muscles take over to go farther in that direction). "EXTENSION" means that the muscle has been positioned at the peak of its backward range of motion (before other muscles take over to go farther in that direction).

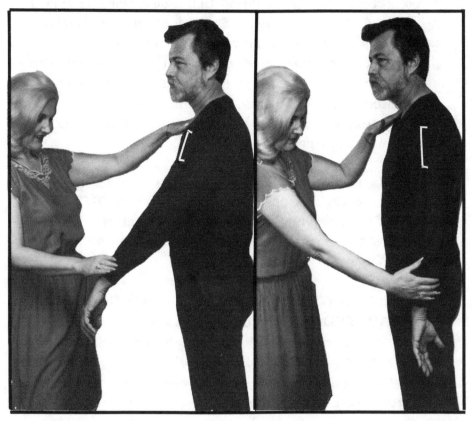

Anatomically, contraction = the lessening of distance between a muscle's origin and insertion. Extension = the significant increase of distance between a muscle's origin and insertion.

PROCEDURE

To begin with, we suggest you use the Anterior Deltoid muscle - shown in the illustration - for practice purposes. As you can see from the photos, Anterior Deltoid's contracted and extended positions are simple and easy to work with.

However, before you actually begin this procedure, find out if your testee has any condition that would make testing a given muscle uncomfortable. **Should such a condition exist, don't test that muscle.** And even if the person gives unqualified acceptance, check further. Position the muscle you want to test in its contracted state and ask your testee, "Is it OK to test your arm in this position? Is this position comfortable to work with?" Proceed ONLY when you receive positive permission.

If there's any question about using the Anterior Deltoid, glance ahead (in this chapter) to THE FIVE INDICATORS OF CHOICE we employ in ONE BRAIN. If Anterior Deltoid presents a problem, try one of the other four - but always receive permission before you proceed.

> **SPECIAL NOTE: Be sure your testee's fingers stay SEPARATED while you test.** For reasons you'll discover later in ONE BRAIN, closed-hand positions can short-circuit the body's communication lines. Make it a point to advise your testee, "Keep your hand open, fingers apart, during the test."

As TESTOR, position your testee's Anterior Deltoid in its CONTRACTED state. Place your hand on that arm <u>above the wrist</u> and complete the testing circuit by stabilizing your body with your other hand on your partner's shoulder (as per illustration). Alert your partner that you're ready to begin by saying, "Hold."

Now apply sssllllooowww <u>GENTLE</u> pressure toward the indicated range-of-motion, but ONLY TO THE POINT YOU FEEL THE MUSCLE HOLD - about "one travelling <u>inch</u>" of movement. The hold-point is a firming up of the muscle's response, a thus-far-and-no-farther sensation, beyond which you'd have to exert force to move that muscle - or your testee would have to forcibly resist your testing pressure to maintain that position. Just go for that holding-ness sensation. Once you've found it, maintain contact for a second before you release the pressure sssllllooowwwllllyyy while keeping physical contact.

NOTE: BREATHE!
While muscle testing - or being tested - we all tend to hold our breath. Relax. Keep breathing. And make sure your partner keeps breathing, too. Holding your breath blocks accurate feedback - SO BREATHE!

The indicator you're testing will either "hold" or feel "mushy," then give way. If you're not altogether certain of the result, BREATHE AND HAVE YOUR PARTNER BREATHE, say "Hold" and test again. Some testees may choose to resist rather than simply hold. They seem to believe that an indicator CHANGE indicates weakness and therefore struggle against allowing the indicator to change. Especially true of those with machismo attitudes, such folk may need to be told "a muscle test isn't a battle of I win/you lose."

The testee's job: simply hold the test position and HAVE NO EXPECTATION other than interest in the outcome. The same is true for you as testor: HAVE NO EXPECTATION other than interest in the outcome of your testing.

At this point, an indicator change represents no more than an under-energy muscular response. The result isn't important other than as a result. Whether the muscle holds strong or goes mushy and gives way, you now have feedback from the body, and you're ready to proceed with testing the whole Anterior Deltoid Circuit.

STEP ONE
As per the illustration, retest the RIGHT Anterior Deltoid in CONTRACTION. Then test the LEFT Anterior Deltoid in contraction and note the result. Those results may well differ. For right now, only the result matters, not its possible implication.

STEP TWO
To complete your check-out of the Anterior Deltoid Circuit, you'll now test the same muscle in EXTENSION. As per the illustration, position the RIGHT arm and test - noting the results - and then the LEFT.

Testing in extension simply reverses the test direction. As you "pushed down and back" on the contracted muscle, you'll "pull up and forward" when testing Anterior Deltoid in extension. Apply the pull-pressure ABOVE the wrist. (Never test on a joint because it might add variables that confuse results - what if the person had arthritis for example?)

So now, having tested one muscle circuit in both contraction and extension, it's time to familiarize yourself with the other four indicators you might find yourself using in the ONE BRAIN process.

THE FIVE INDICATORS OF CHOICE
Arm muscles are easiest for testing most people, so we've included pectoralis major clavicular, anterior deltoid, supraspinatus and latissimus dorsi to find the one best suited to your partner's (and your own) comfort as a

testee. But should you discover an under-energy state in arm muscles, we've included one leg muscle - quadriceps - as another possibility. All five muscles are shown in the illustrations, together with the testing positions.

Check them ALL out on your testee, each in turn - in contraction right and left, then in extension right and left.

Your pressure will follow the natural arc of the arm or the leg. See the illustration.

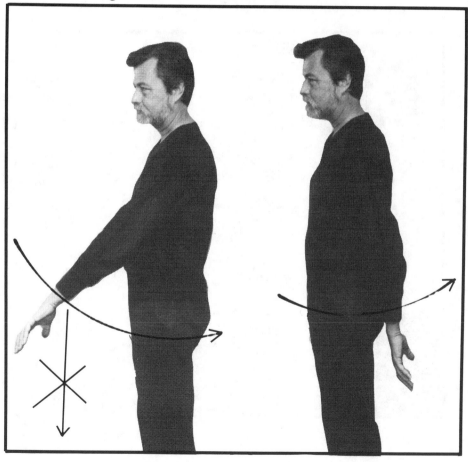

THE FIVE MUSCLES

PECTORALIS MAJOR CLAVICULAR

Contraction: position your testee's arm straight out from the shoulder (parallel to the floor), with thumb down and palm out. Your test direction is down/out.

Extension: position the arm (thumb down, palm out) 45 degrees down/out from the hip. Test direction is up/in toward the contracted position.

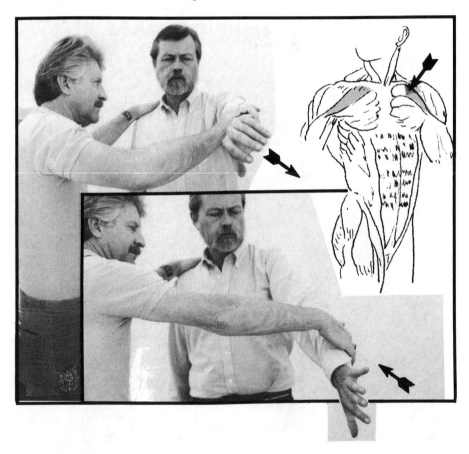

LATISSIMUS DORSI

Contraction: position the arm straight down, wrist turned so the palm is outward. Be sure that the elbow is straight and the torso hasn't changed position. Your test direction is straight out to the side.

Extension: position the arm 45 degrees straight out from the side, palm still facing out. Test direction is directly in toward the side.

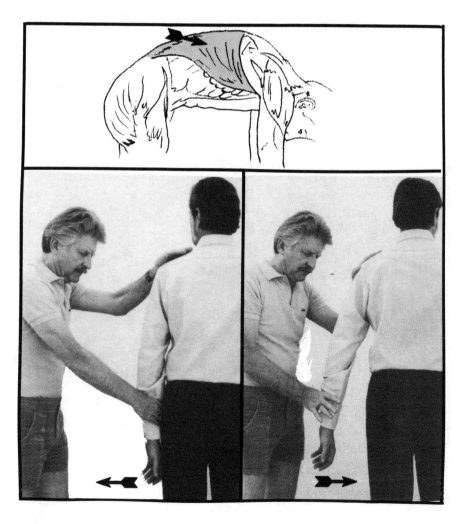

ANTERIOR DELTOID

Contraction: position the arm forward and raised 30 degrees with palm down. Your test direction is downward, back toward the body.

Extension: position the arm straight downward, palm back. Test direction is forward/upward.

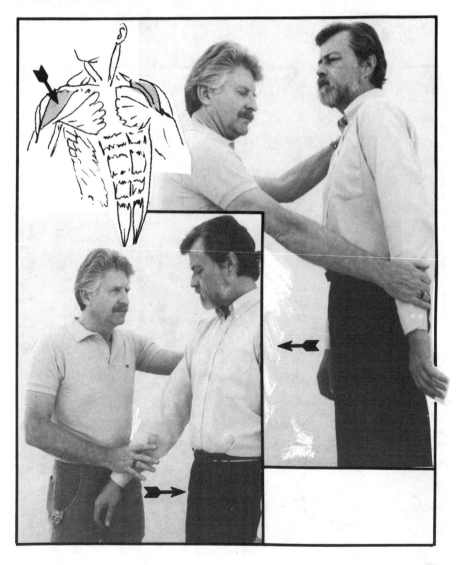

SUPRASPINATUS

Contraction: position the arm some 20 degrees forward/outward. Your test direction is in toward the midline and down.

Extension: position the arm downward toward the midline. Test direction: up/outward.

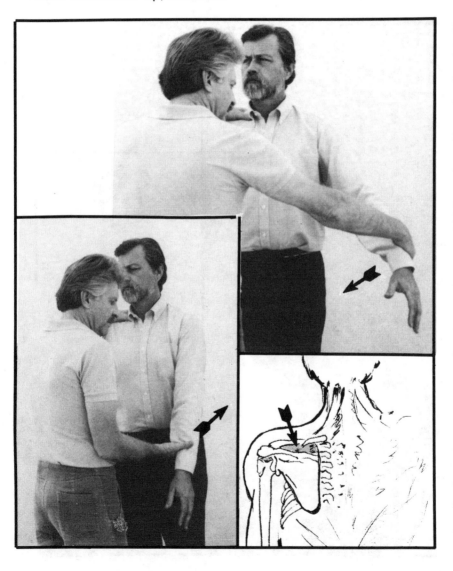

QUADRICEPS

Contraction: position the leg with knee parallel to hip, foot slightly forward of 90 degrees. Your test direction is straight downward.

Extension: knee straight down, foot back and down slightly of 90 degrees. Test direction is forward and up.

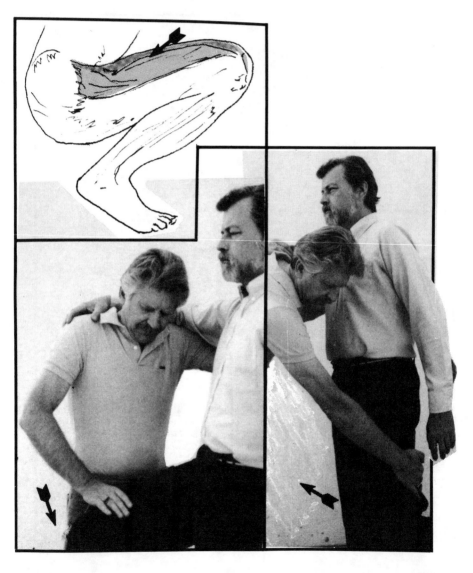

And now - **congratulations!**

Even if you're absolutely new to muscle testing, with your partner you've done more research on muscle circuits than have many practitioners of the art. Most testers content themselves with merely checking the contracted position of ONE muscle on ONE side of the body before assuming they have a valid test. And there's more: you now have the potential of retrieving TWICE as much information from the muscles tested.

In the process of checking five muscles in both contraction and extension, you probably discovered there were DIFFERENCES right and left as well as in the contracted/extended positions. Those differences mean a reduction in the quality of feedback from the body, should you use a non-consistent muscle. What you want is a muscle indicator that "holds strong" on both sides and in both positions.

Still, even when you've found such a "hold strong in all positions" indicator, there's more to check out before trusting that muscle to give you the accurate responses that make further tests valid. This is particularly true if ALL FIVE MUSCLES held strong in all positions. When everything holds strong, there may be "interference on the line" in the form of an over-all blockage of the system due to stress. As testors, we want to be sure we're working with a CLEAR MUSCLE CIRCUIT prior to actually testing for specifics.

CIRCUITS - WHAT THEY ARE
AND HOW THEY'RE BLOCKED

DEFINITION

A **Circuit** is a flow pathway through which activating/deactivating signals are transmitted. Any given circuit has its own individual integrity, even when forming part of another more complex circuit.

There are many different kinds of circuits in the body, but for our purposes one illustration tells the basic story. An example of a neurological circuit is the complex process of walking. When we perform that activity, every movement - simple or elaborate - is a sequence of skeletal muscle contraction and extension by means of an intricate interplay between nerve and muscle. The "command" is initiated in the brain and conveyed over millions of neurons to the muscles involved.

In walking, when you bring your right foot forward, the left arm also comes forward. The neural impulses stimulating your right leg to move forward also inhibit opposing muscle groups (antagonist muscles) to allow that leg its forward motion. The same thing happens to your left arm. So while in a walking stance position, the inhibited muscles will test "weak" while the stimulated muscles test "strong."

When you checked anterior deltoid in both contraction and extension you were, in effect, checking the whole "walking circuit" because you were checking a part of it. The same was true when you checked pectoralis major clavicular and quadriceps. In fact, when you perform any muscle test, you activate many more muscles than the one "in hand" - you're involving every muscle on that circuit to some degree.

BLOCKED CIRCUITS

Physical and emotional stressors produce the same affects within the body because the brain processes both "real and imagined experience" in exactly the same way. (Which explains why FEAR OF PAIN is as real as pain itself.) So, should part of a given circuit's muscle network give way to emotional stress or physical strain, THE REST OF THAT CIRCUIT ATTEMPTS TO COMPENSATE, THE EFFORT OF WHICH BLOCKS THE FREE-FLOW OF ITS USUAL OPERATION. In effect, it's "trying too hard" to do its job, which means it can't do its job as effectively.

If you're testing a muscle that's part of a blocked circuit, it's very likely to test "strong" when it really isn't. And it will read "strong" in both extension and contraction, too. The only test result you'll have is a hearty YES! to everything. For this reason, we make sure the indicator muscle has a Clear Circuit before any further testing. This all-important double-check insures the best possible test results. Without it, we'd have real reason to doubt the effectiveness of muscle testing.

A CLEAR CIRCUIT INDICATOR MUSCLE

DEFINITION

A Clear Circuit Indicator Muscle holds in both contraction and extension and then can be sedated, which in turn effects the same muscle on the opposite side of the body.

In the belly (fullest portion) of each muscle, sensory nerve endings called proprioceptors give that muscle information about movement and position. Pushing the belly of the muscle together causes the proprioceptors to send a sedation message to the muscle, relaxing it. Spreading the belly of the muscle apart causes the proprioceptors to send a tonification message, strengthening the muscle.

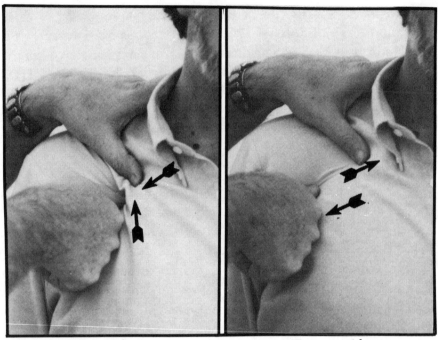

To sedate   To tonify

PROCEDURE
STEP ONE
To make sure of the clearest results, have the testee stand in a relaxed state for the tests, with the only body movement being that which is necessary for the testing itself. Test the indicator muscle on both sides of the body and in both positions following this pattern:

Test in CONTRACTION on one side of the body, then in EXTENSION on the other. Repeat, reversing the muscle's test position on each side of the body. The indicator muscle should hold strong in both positions on both sides of the body. (If it doesn't, for purposes of this exercise, find an indicator muscle that does.)

STEP TWO

Verify that you have a Clear Circuit indicator. Go to the belly of the muscle (see illustration for location) and GENTLY BUT FIRMLY PUSH IT TOGETHER moving in the same direction as the muscle fibers. If the muscle's fibers travel vertically, push in on the vertical; if they run on a diagonal, follow the same direction.

RETEST - the indicator should reverse its response from strong to "weak." If it has, you've found a Clear Circuit. (If it hasn't the circuit is blocked. Go to the next section for information on how to unblock it.)

STEP THREE

Restore balance to the circuit. Go back to the belly of the muscle you sedated and GENTLY BUT FIRMLY SPREAD IT APART in the direction of its origin and insertion points.

RETEST - the indicator should now hold strong in both contraction and extension, and you're ready to proceed with further testing.

NOTE: When manipulating the proprioceptors in the belly of a muscle, your intention has more power than applying extra force. Simply push/spread with gentle but firm pressure two or three times before retesting. Don't work at it; if the circuit's blocked, it's blocked.

CORRECTING A BLOCKED CIRCUIT

When a muscle does not respond to the above procedure and you want to restore its normal communication, use the following procedure.

STEP ONE
Place the indicator muscle in CONTRACTION and have your testee forcefully pull down toward EXTENSION while you pull upward into CONTRACTION even more.

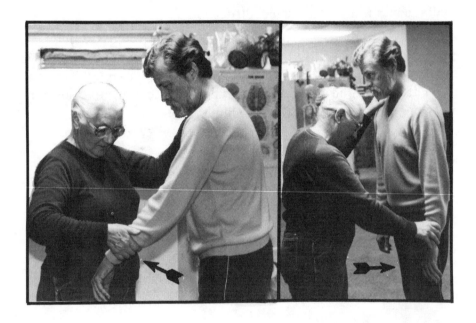

Now go to the other side of the body and place the same indicator muscle in EXTENSION and have your testee forcefully push up toward CONTRACTION while you push firmly downward toward EXTENSION even more.

STEP TWO
Reverse the same indicator's position to CONTRACTION and repeat the procedure. Then unblock the other side of the body with the indicator in EXTENSION.

STEP THREE
Now repeat the sedation procedure, pushing the proprioceptors in the belly of the muscle together GENTLY BUT FIRMLY on one side of the body.

RETEST in CONTRACTION. The indicator should not hold, but weaken. The same will be true of EXTENSION on the other side of the body. RETEST to make sure.

Now sedate the indicator's other half, and RETEST. Both right and left indicators should not hold now, either in contracted or extended positions.

STEP FOUR
Restore your indicator's normal communication by spreading the spindle cells in the belly of that muscle - and anchor the correction by RETESTING. The muscle should now hold in both extension and contraction on both sides of the body. You've successfully unblocked the circuit and restored its normal communication!

NOTE: The unblocking procedure outlined above works most of the time. However, when someone's in deep emotional or physical stress, a circuit may stay blocked (in the moment) and can't be sedated no matter what technique you use - magnets, sedation points, spindle cells, etc. So if the unblocking procedure doesn't work, simply use another muscle for your indicator. At least one of the five will be available for reliable Clear Circuit testing.

SKILLS REINFORCEMENT

To reinforce your awareness of how indicator muscles respond, take each of the five indicators in turn and check them for Clear Circuits. Unblock as needed. What you discover is less important than the fact of discovery. The more you test, the more you learn from testing.

EFFECTIVE TESTING/YOU AS THE TESTOR

Even if you're a complete novice at muscle testing, you can get excellent results by observing the following groundrules (once you have a Clear Circuit indicator muscle):

ONE: ATTUNEMENT

In actuality, a muscle test is nothing more or less than TUNING IN to your testee's energy field. TOUCH can bring attunement if you tune yourself OUT of the picture and put your undivided attention on the test. Have no expectations other than being AWARE of the indicator muscle changing. It's as simple as that.

TWO: ASSURANCE

Trust your test-ability. Be assured both you and your testee will get results. Assured of that, appreciate the connection being made by your gentle, attuned testing-touch.

Preface each test by saying "Hold" - to alert your partner that you're ready to begin. And, to guarantee your own calm assurance, as you begin each test, inhale deeply. EXHALE as you make the actual test itself.

THREE: INTEREST

Demonstrate your INTEREST in the testee by using gentle sssslllooowww pressure during each test - and by staying in touch-contact with the indicator muscle for a second BEFORE the test, and for a second or two AFTER releasing the test pressure. This continued contact shows your interest and your assurance. Most of all, it keeps you ATTUNED to your testee's energy.

> REMINDER: be sure your testee's hands stay relaxed and open, with fingers apart, while you test.

EFFECTIVE "BEING TESTED"/YOU AS THE TESTEE

If you've never been muscle tested - or even if you have - the same three basic groundrules apply. ATTUNEMENT, ASSURANCE and INTEREST.

ATTUNEMENT

Choose to ATTUNE to your own body. Put yourself in an ATTUNED state of mind. Once your indicator is in position, simply stabilize it there. Attune to it, and maintain that attunement. Have NO EXPECTATIONS, just BE there.

ASSURANCE

Be assured you'll get results. The only possible stumbling block would be your FEAR of being tested, or a fear about "not being in control." Forget such foolishness (and that's exactly what it is). Consciously give yourself the command: "CHOOSE TO BE TEST-ABLE." When your testor says "Hold," inhale - then EXHALE slowly as the test begins and continue to exhale until the test pressure is released.

Keep your hand open and relaxed, fingers well apart while being tested. Closed hand positions can short circuit the body's electrical system and produce misinformation.

INTEREST

Get really INTERESTED in discovering what your body has to tell you. The process is truly fascinating and, as you're about to find out, SO VERY ILLUMINATING!

A DEMONSTRATION OF EMOTION'S POWER TO AFFECT THE BODY

Before actually testing people who have no experience with muscle testing, it's helpful to demonstrate the impact emotional stress has on the body. This demonstration lets them experience the procedure and shows them how to recognize its RESULTS. (It's also an excellent addition to any presentation that involves muscle testing.)

STEP ONE

Always begin by asking permission to make the test AND checking to be sure the person has no physical problems that would make the test uncomfortable. Then establish your credentials by finding a Clear Circuit indicator muscle. Go through the whole procedure. Not only does this assure you that the test results are valid, it also gives the person practice as a testee. More: the person has an opportunity to experience what a change in the indicator feels like.

STEP TWO

When you know you have a Clear Circuit indicator, ask your testee to select a past experience which was really upsetting - "gut-wrenching" - such as being made to look a fool, or being criticized in public, betrayed by a lover or losing something important. **This incident does NOT need to be verbalized, just remembered.**

Now ask, "Would you please close your eyes and put that memory back in mind. Re-live it until you can FEEL it in your stomach. Nod when you have that feeling."

Once the nod comes, RETEST the indicator in contraction moving toward extension, then in extension moving toward contraction, and see if there's a change in response. Nine times out of ten, the indicator will attest to a change.

STEP THREE

Just as dramatic, here comes the second part of this demonstration. Having established that the indicator changes just by recalling a past stressor, say, "Now would you please recall an experience that brought joy, happiness, great relief or real pleasure. Again, verbalizing isn't necessary. Close your eyes and re-live that happy memory. Nod when you have its feeling."

When you get the nod - RETEST, both contraction and extension. The indicator will stay strong in both positions.

Now have the person re-live the negative experience again, and TEST. The indicator will be weak in all positions. Then have the person replace the negative experience with the positive experience and re-live it again, and TEST. The indicator will now hold strong in all positions.

NEGATIVE EMOTIONAL CHARGE = DISORIENTATION WITHIN THE BODY

A strong indicator demonstrates that the body is staying well-organized in regards to a given test category or to recalled or anticipated situations. A weak test response means the category or recalled/anticipated situation causes emotional overwhelm, with its accompanying muscular disorganization. Muscular disorganization is a reliable indication of stress's "overwhelming" power.

WHAT A HOLD STRONG RESPONSE TELLS YOU
1 -   The issue tested lacks sufficient Negative Emotional Charge to make the indicator change.
2 -   When asking direct questions, a "hold strong" means a positive ("yes") answer.
3 -   A Blocked Circuit (due to an intense subconscious desire to block feedback on the issue being tested). Correct immediately.

WHAT AN INDICATOR CHANGE TELLS YOU
1 -   The issue tested has enough Negative Emotional Charge to weaken the muscle, thereby indicating a priority for correction.
2 -   When asking direct questions, an indicator change means a negative ("no") answer.
      Switching (due to the amount of fear attached to the issue). Correct immediately.

What's so stunning to us, is that Clear Circuit muscle testing goes beyond opinions to assess our true integrated body/mind reaction to any given stressor. This is particularly valuable to know because frontal brain function reduces in quality under stress and, in such a state, our mental evaluations are rarely reliable.

And, using Clear Circuit muscle testing, we may discover that what we considered a minor stressor actually puts us in overwhelm, while major stressors don't have the effect we expected them to have upon our systems. For instance, it may not be having to turn in a series of reports that "blows us out," but the stress of having to look up so many words because we spell so poorly!

Plus, the fine-tuning of a muscle test can bring to light stressors we've felt, yet never verbalized or thought through. Sometimes, just knowing the SPECIFIC cause of stress gives the brain enough data to resolve the problem AND the negative emotion attached to it.

STRESS AND DOMINANT BRAIN DYSLEXIA

The ALTERNATE Brain takes care of AUTOMATIC responses in the body. It carries out spatial and rhythmic tasks. Dominant does the verbalizing. In silence, or to music, Alternate accomplishes all kinds of intricate activities. The second we open our mouths to speak, we're at the mercy of Dominant CIA's limitations and ALL the emotions attached to verbal conflict. Few of us can talk and DO at the same time (other than habitually anchored activities, of course).

When we're threatened by pain or fear - in whatever form they present themselves - Alternate just hums along happily, keeping the body in harmony with whatever specifics CIA has planned for the day. But the micro-second that pain, fear or fear of pain crops up, CIA goes into its shut-down/survival/fight or flight mode and tunes out Alternate's supportive integration of body/mind activities.

To test the hypothesis that certain brain activities interfere with others, Marcel Kinsbourne (THE BRAIN, THE LAST FRONTIER by Richard M. Restak, MD) "taught his experimental subjects to balance a small metal rod on their index fingers. After they became practiced at this simple task, Kinsbourne challenged them by requiring the repetition of a series of test phrases. He found that the performance of the subjects' left hand was not affected by speaking, but the balancing performance of the right hand deteriorated dramatically. Since both speaking and right hand performance use the same hemisphere (the left), Kinsbourne reasoned that the activity of one interfered with the other. He repeated the experiment, only this time with children as young as 3 years. Results were the same."

If one brain hemisphere becomes stressed, the muscles on the opposite side will give a weak response due to non-integration of its signals. In effect, that's exactly what you'll be testing when you go through the examination which follows. **All learning dysfunctions are related to speech in some form, verbal or written, spoken or heard – and all dysfunctions in the learning process were caused by emotional stress in the form of fear, pain or fear of pain at the time of the learning.** In fact, that's what we learned. More accurately, that's what our Dominant CIA "learned."

Now it's time to unlearn that learning and learn how to learn to learn, free of the past stressors that made us believe we couldn't!

IDENTIFYING DYSLEXIC LEARNING DYSFUNCTIONS:
THE EXAMINATION

DEFINITION

A series of tests to identify the neurological short-circuits within the Dominant Brain Hemisphere, and between the hemispheres, which result in dyslexic learning dysfunctions.

We present only the examination in this section of the book. For the moment, that's the whole focus. Beyond the few corrections that need to be made in the first test categories, all correction procedures will be covered in a subsequent chapter.

EXPLANATION

Understand that the word "examination" itself produces stress in almost everybody - a stress that's been building since the first time we understood what "test" and "examination" meant in terms of grade-getting. Immediately you start testing, you key-in the memory neurons related to the learning process. This focused stress keeps every response on that single target.

PROCEDURE

Having identified a Clear Circuit indicator muscle, use Dominant's arm for test purposes, since "the hand you write with" accesses the brain's language centers with almost all of us.

Test each of the examination's categories in sequence and, for each, check the indicator in BOTH contraction and extension, unless we tell you otherwise.

Basic ONE BRAIN EXAMINATION

Make all tests in **CONTRACTION** and **EXTENSION** using **BOTH** arms.

Chap 2-3   STAGES OF STRESS   YES   NO   Lvl #1   Lvl #2   Lvl #3   Lvl #4
Chap 3-16   CLEAR CIRCUIT INDICATOR MUSCLE _____

Correct the following, if necessary, before proceeding with the tests.
Chap 4-3   SWITCHING
Chap 4-7   CENTRAL MERIDIAN and GOVERNING MERIDIAN

NO CORRECTIONS WITH THE BALANCE OF THE EXAMINATION,
———— ONLY INDICATE IF A CORRECTION IS NEEDED ————

TEST   REMARKS
Chap 5-1   SET STANDARDS (Negative Emotional Charge 1 - 100%)
By Others_____ %
For Others_____ %   _____
For Self _____ %   _____
Chap 5-5   READING PERCEPTION: (Read while testing)   _____
Forward   _____
Backward   _____
Silently   _____
Comprehension   _____
Alphabet   _____
Numbers 0-10   _____
Chap 5-8   CROSSING MID-LINE (write sentence on back of sheet and test)
L Midline R (Contraction)   L Midline R (Extension)
Chap 5-12   SHORT-CIRCUIT EYES:
Eyes Open (Left Right Up Down Mid-line)   _____
Eyes Closed (Left Right Up down Mid-line)   _____
Eyes Open (Near, Arms' length, Far)   _____
Eyes back/forth 20 times   _____
Chap 5-16   SHORT-CIRCUIT EARS (turn head)   _____
Chap 5-19   FIXATION TEST (black paper)   _____
Chap 5-24   CROSS-PATTERNING:
Cross-patterning   _____
X (Should hold strong)   _____
II (should not hold strong)   _____
Chap 5-28   HYOID (gently move while testing)   _____
Chap 5-30   TRANSVERSE FLOW   _____
Chap 5-32   NUTRITION/GENETIC (Touch glabella)   _____
Chap 5-34   CIA (tap/hold behind dominant ear)   _____
Chap 5-36   EMOTIONAL STRESS STATEMENT
Positive: "I want and trust my ability to _____ "
Negative: "I do not want and do not trust my ability to _____ "
                                            _____ %

SWITCHING TESTS

DEFINITION
Tests to determine whether internal or external stress is blocking clear communication between left and right brain hemispheres and thus confusing nerve and energy patterns in the body. When muscle tested in a "switched" condition, the body responds with erroneous and/or "reversed" information.

TESTS
  A. GENERAL TEST FOR SWITCHING:
  1. Test the indicator muscle first with one hand (read: "one polarity"), then the other hand (read: "the other polarity"). If the muscle goes weak when you change hands, the person is "switched" in one or all of the modes outlined below.

  2. Now test both arms simultaneously, then change hands (cross one over the other) and test both arms at the same time again. If the indicators go weak, the person is "switched" on two of the following modes:

  B. SPECIFIC TEST:
  1. To discover if the switch is from ONE SIDE OF THE BODY/BRAIN TO THE OTHER, touch K-27 with index and second finger together first on the right and TEST, then on the left and TEST. K-27 is found just below the clavical close to the sternum. (See illustration. "K" = Kidney Meridian. "27" = the 27th (and final) acupuncture point on that meridian.)

2. To discover if the switch is from the body's TOP TO BOTTOM, touch just above the upper lip (on the midline) with index and second fingertips together and TEST. Repeat, touching just below the lower lip on the midline. (See illustration).

3. To discover if the switch is from the body/brain's FRONT TO BACK, touch the navel with the same fingertips and TEST. Repeat, touching the coccyx while testing. (See illustration).

CORRECTION

Place one hand over the navel, and with the other hand rub the touch-points that caused the change. Reverse hands and repeat. (People can make these corrections for themselves.)

EXPLANATION

The "switching" phenomenon usually indicates that Dominant's CIA can't handle what's happening on the conscious, subconscious or body levels of awareness. Usually, during a muscle test, the closer you come to "the answer," the more likely a person is to switch. Threatened, the CIA elects to produce erroneous information that'll get it off the hook.

It's as important to check for SWITCHING as to be sure you have a Clear Circuit test indicator muscle. From now on, make it your ritual to 1) identify a Clear Circuit indicator, and 2) check for Switching PRIOR TO THE START OF ANY TESTING SESSION.

Also, be warned! During a test session, certain folk are more than likely to Switch. At that point, the information becomes flaky, inconsistent or downright contradictory. Whenever you as TESTOR begin to feel confused by the results you're getting, CHECK FOR SWITCHING immediately, and correct the condition if it exists.

Under the most intense stress, your testee's CIA might elect to actually BLOCK the circuit of which the indicator muscle is a part. All at once, every test will hold strong. If that kind of pattern appears, check the circuit to see if it's still clear.

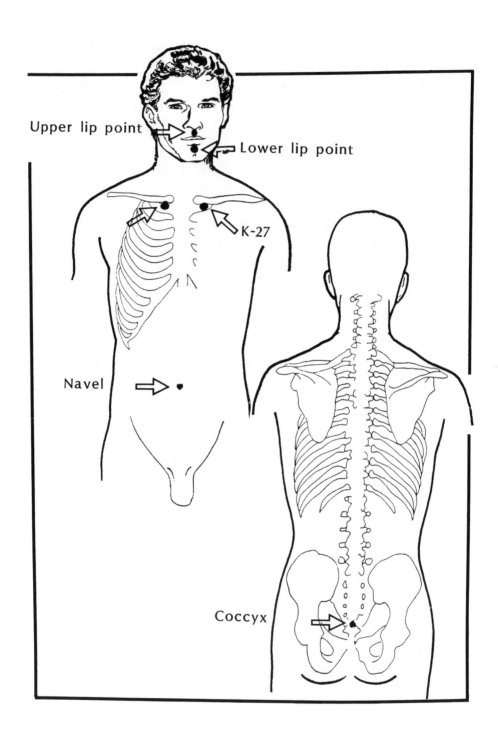

Upper lip point

Lower lip point

K-27

Navel

Coccyx

CENTRAL/GOVERNING MERIDIAN TESTING

DEFINITION:

A test to evaluate whether the energy flows of the Central and Governing Meridians are normal.

TEST:

1. CENTRAL MERIDIAN: With you hand, trace upward from the pubic bone to the lower lip and TEST. The indicator should hold strong in both contraction and extension.

2. Reverse direction, start with the lower lip and trace downward to the pubic bone and TEST again. The indicator should change in both test positions.

If the Central Meridian's flow is abnormal, your test results will reverse and the indicator will change during Step One, and hold strong during Step Two. Correction is indicated, but check the Governing Meridian's flow first.

3. GOVERNING MERIDIAN: Repeat the previous pattern, only for this meridian, your first step will be to trace upward from the coccyx over the top of the head and down to the upper lip, then TEST. The indicator should hold strong.

Reverse direction, start at the upper lip and trace back over the top of the head and downward to the coccyx, then TEST. The indicator should change.

If Governing Meridian's flow is abnormal, your test results will be reversed. Correction is indicated. Make the correction immediately.

CORRECTION

"Flush" the meridian by moving your hand rapidly up and down the meridian flow-path. Do this several times, ending at the lips. Then RETEST to verify correction.

EXPLANATION

According to ancient Chinese medicine, the life force flows through established pathways in the body and have a direct relationship to such vital phenomena as growth, metabolism, organs and nervous system functions.

This energy is integral to the human body and asserts itself in the form of an "essence." This essence exists within everything in the universe. It is the origin of all things, (the very cause of life itself.) In a kidney, for example, it exists as the "essence of the kidney"; in vascular circulation, it exists as the "essence of the circulating blood." It is this essence which sustains the body, which causes it to move and to live.

When a meridian becomes either debilitated or over stressed, both the internal organs and the nervous system suffer accordingly.

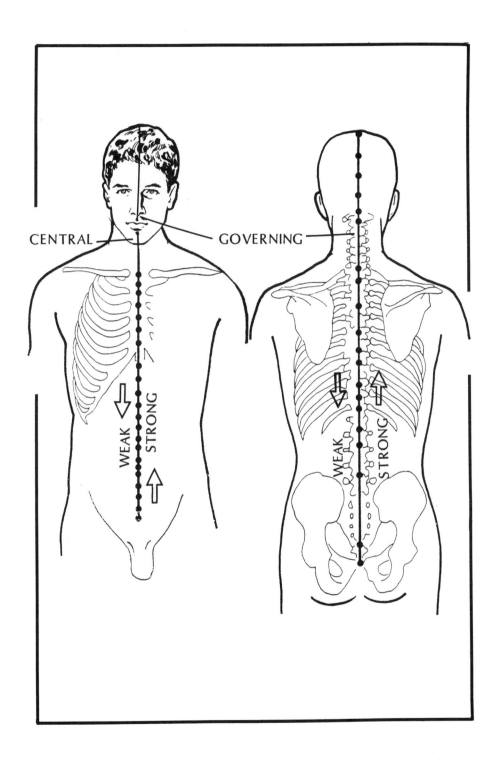

CONTINUE THE EXAMINATION
WITH <u>NO</u> FURTHER CORRECTIONS
AT THIS TIME.

WHEN "SET STANDARDS" CAUSE STRESS

DEFINITION

A test to determine the percentage of Negative Emotional Charge a person feels when constrained to meet measurable standards of performance.

As demonstrated by muscle testing itself, **Negative Emotional Charge** inhibits motor skills and lowers energy. When you face a test of any kind - whether in academics, sports, sales, relationships or life itself - the standard you "have to" meet in order to WIN may trigger enough **Negative Emotional Charge** to make you LOSE. For example, "In order to pass, you'll have to answer 80 out out of 100 questions," or "solve 10 out of 12 math problems," or spell 30 out of 35 words correctly." Such set standards can cause sufficient stress to blank the memory and/or crimp physical performance.

No matter who sets the standards (others for you, you for yourself or you for others), "SET STANDARDS" becomes a major issue. Identifying and defusing the **% Negative Emotional Charge** involved promotes increased skill and energy in any competitive activity.

To identify the % of Negative Emotional Charge, simply test from 0 to 100 in increments of 10. Example: Say "0 to 10" and test; "10 to 20" and test (etc.). When the indicator changes, you've gone beyond the SPECIFIC percentage point - so test backward from the highest number, one numeral at a time. Let's say, the indicator changed on "80 to 90." Take it from the top: "90" and test; "89" and test; "88" and test. The SPECIFIC number will affirm itself and the muscle will hold STRONG.

TEST

1. Say, "I'm going to test for the percentage of Negative Emotional Charge you feel when OTHERS set the standards for you." (Give a "for instance" appropriate to your testee's experience.) Now TEST: "0 to 10" and continue until the indicator changes. Then test backward from the highest number until the indicator holds strong. Note that percentage point in the "BY OTHERS" blank on the exam form.

2. Ask your testee "What's something in which you really want to excel where you set the standards for yourself. Sports, art, writing, a hobby - what?" Once that's been identified: SAY, "So now we'll test for whatever % of Negative Emotional Charge you have when YOU set the standards for yourself." Test "0 to 10" and on up toward 100 until the indicator changes, then back from the highest number (numeral by numeral) until the indicator affirms "Yes, that's it, all right" by holding STRONG. Put the appropriate % in the "BY SELF" blank.

3. Identify an area where your testee sets the standards for others. (Even little children know this one, by the way - for example in minding a younger brother or sister, or as the "authority" in a game or sport no matter how young the players.) Once you've identified a specific, Say, "So now we'll test for the % of Negative Emotional Charge when you set the standard for OTHERS." Proceed as above,

from 0 upward in increments of 10 until the indicator changes, then test backward until it holds strong. Put that number in the "FOR OTHERS" blank."

NOTE: Some people may have 0% of Negative Emotional Charge on one or more of these issues. However, if the indicator does NOT change, check that you still have a Clear Circuit Muscle to test. As a matter of fact, if <u>any</u> test result seems inappropriate, unlikely, inconsistent or just plain screwy, **always <u>assure</u> yourself that you have a Clear Circuit.** Blocking and Switching may come hand in hand with negative emotions.

<u>% OF NEGATIVE EMOTIONAL CHARGE</u>

Identify the % of Negative Charge for all major issues that come up in the defusion process. It helps our <u>awareness</u> of how much stress attaches to that issue in the first place - as well as <u>verifying positive change</u> when the % drops to 0 after defusion.

EXPLANATION

In SOCIOBIOLOGY, Wilson states, "The hypothalamic-limbic complex taxes the conscious mind with ambivalence whenever the body's organization encounters a stressful situation." That "ambivalence" multiplies over the years and turns into reaction patterns aimed at survival, but based on Negative Emotional Charge.

When it comes to "learning disabilities," just imagine little children going to school for the first time. Before they walk in the door, they're already in stress from being away from home and parents, meeting peers and adults who have the power to make them meet arbitrary standards many times a day. Look at all the fear, pain and fear of pain they're under at the very beginning of the formal "learning" process! No wonder their little brain's turn off, their eyes dim from what they don't want to see, their ears "block" from what they don't want to hear. Right away, they start setting up physical complaints to use as excuses to get out of taking tests, one of which is SCHOOL itself - not to mention having to deal with peers they don't like.

"I don't feel good today and want to stay home." How many of us have used some form of that basic excuse over the years to get out of what we don't want to do - work, appointments, parties, you name it?

Since infant emotional reactions become CIA commands from then on, when you test **% of Negative Charge,** you discover the results of a person's childhood decree about how specific stressors affect the body. Such decrees REMAIN in operation until we defuse them of negative emotion - not just in the present, but in the past at the moment that we made them. Defusing only the present leaves the past still in power.

READING FORWARD	STRONG C-E	WEAK C-E
READING BACKWARD	STRONG C-E	WEAK C-E
READING SILENTLY	STRONG C-E	WEAK C-E
COMPREHENSION	STRONG C-E	WEAK C-E
SAYING ALPHABET	STRONG C-E	WEAK ON C-E_____

READING PERCEPTION TESTS

DEFINITION

A series of tests which indicate the degree of stress relating to the act of reading and reading comprehension.

TEST:

Test each of the following four skills in turn. Test each as a separate category.

This time, you'll be testing a bit differently, inasmuch as your testee will be reading longer than for the usual muscle test. So keep contact with the indicator muscle throughout the whole time. Once the person begins to read, apply test pressure until the indicator changes. When it does, immediately release the test pressure (but continue to maintain contact). Re-stabilize the muscle into the test position and apply test pressure again. Continue this pattern throughout the length of time the person is reading. Alternately test, then re-stabilize and test again.

1. Have the person READ FORWARD aloud while testing.

2. Have the person READ BACKWARD aloud while testing.

8-11

3. Have the person READ SILENTLY while testing.

4. FOR COMPREHENSION, have the person read aloud while testing, then give feedback on what was just read, while testing.

5. For the ALPHABET, have the person recite the alphabet one letter at a time and test. Go through the entire alphabet this way. Record which letters make the indicator change.

EXPLANATION

The process of SIGHT involves a myriad of nerve-relays to the brain's visual areas, but that's not all. In addition, other nerve-relays go from the retina to brain areas that have to do with the physical process of seeing, such as movement of the eyes, head, neck and body - not to mention other areas that move the eye toward anything heard, modify the size of the pupil in regard to available light, or change the convexity of the lens.

When you hand someone something and say, "Look at this!" - you can see the eyes roll inward and downward and the pupils contract. Begin to APPRECIATE the thousands of separate body/brain functions that coordinate to make such perception possible. When you add all the additional body/brain activity involved in reading, comprehension and remembering plus the stressors these activities may represent, you can understand the involvement of such skills.

Correction on page 8-10

NUMBERS PERCEPTION TEST

DEFINITION

A test to indicate the degree of stress numbers create in the system.

TEST

Follow the same procedure as for testing the ALPHABET, only this time you'll test each number from 0 to 9. Be sure to test in both contraction and extension on this and ALL examination categories, and note any differences you discover.

EXPLANATION

We use a different part of our brain to process mathematics than to process words. This region is in the Dominant hemisphere (usually LEFT), between the regions for organizing speech and visual perception - which indicates that both verbal and visual symbols enter into mathematical thinking. Since the housing of this process resides in other than the language areas, some children who "can't" read, spell or write may be gifted at mathematics - always a confusion and a puzzle for themselves, their parents and teachers.

Correction on page   8-15

CROSSING THE MID-LINE
COMPREHENSION/RETENTION TEST

DEFINITION

A test to identify dyslexic misperception of the written word, a misperception which affects both comprehension and retention.

TEST

To discover if the eyes "short-circuit" when crossing the mid-line:

1.   Have the person write one or two sentences on a flip-chart, chalkboard or piece of paper. When testing children too young to write, have the child draw a picture. Both produce the same results.

2.   Now ask your testee to look only at the right third of what's written while you test BOTH arms in contraction and extension. Then ask your testee to look only at the middle third of what's written while you test BOTH arms in both positions. Last: ask your testee to look only at the left third of the writing and test as previously.

Record all indicator changes on the exam form.

EXPLANATION

Our visual field is approximately 180 degrees. Each eye sees about 120 degrees with an overlap at the mid-line of about 60 degrees. Although both cerebral hemispheres receive information from both eyes, the LEFT hemisphere activates when we look toward the right with the right eye leading. The RIGHT hemisphere activates when we look to the left with the left eye leading. The mid-line area "should" be the area where the two hemispheres integrate the images perceived. Without integration, what one eye/hemisphere perceives can be cancelled out by the other eye/hemisphere. The result? We "can't" comprehend what we read because we haven't seen one whole section of the printed page. And what we can't comprehend we have no reason to retain in memory.

Here's some important background information to help clarify the nature of why and how this kind of misperception takes place.

The two hemispheres operate as two separate mental systems, each with its own capacity to learn, remember, feel emotion and behave. This was proven by researchers testing <u>one half</u> of the brain at a time - something impossible to do with normal brains because both halves are in constant communication. Neurologists have developed a technique, called the Wada test, that allows one hemisphere of the brain to be put to sleep while the other remains awake. It was devised to assure the neurosurgeon that the hemisphere that should be dominant for language is, in fact dominant, before proceeding with major neurosurgery.

Here's the result of one such research project:

A testee has his left brain hemisphere anesthetized. While the RIGHT side of his body is unconscious and immobile,

immobile, the LEFT is capable of movement because the RIGHT brain hemisphere is awake. A spoon is placed in the speechless person's left hand and he is requested to remember it. 30 seconds later, the spoon is removed from his hand.

A few minutes pass and the drug begins to wear off and he is asked, "Can you tell me what was placed in your left hand?" He looks puzzled and denies anything had been placed in his left hand. (This is the usual first response of those who take the test.) He is then shown a group of objects including the spoon. "Of course," comes his quick response "the spoon."

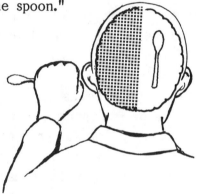

Such testing demonstrates that we can perceive information, record it in one hemisphere which is ready and able to express itself through <u>movement</u> - and at the same time be unavailable from the other half of the brain that handles <u>speech/language</u>.

As we read and write, we're moving our eyes from left to right, passing through a mid-point. When a dyslexic reaches this mid-section, more often than not there's a perception conflict between the two brain hemispheres. LEFT/DOMINANT should take over while RIGHT/ALTERNATE continues to provide the visual

Whatever the cause, if this doesn't happen, we're functionally "blind" at the mid-line. Also, if the brain does "shortcircuit," our eyes may not receive sufficient visual stimulation to trigger impulses clear enough to register within the central nervous system, and the complete message will not get through.

While the latest brain books agree the brain has only two hemispheres - the right and left - the famous scientist-metaphysician Gurdjieff believed we have three "brains," all three of which can be trained, and this training can be generalized so that students will be able to develop their mental faculties to such an extent that a great deal of learning can be accomplished with ease. Presumably Gurdjieff's "third brain" equates with mid-line function: the accurate perception and integration of both the whole and the part.

> AN OBSERVATION YOU MIGHT CARE TO CHECK OUT to help testees recognize dyslexic handwriting: A mid-line "short-circuit" often results in neat writing on one side of the page and not the other. Or writing will be lighter on one side of the page, or lighter in the middle section.

Correction on page 8/16.

SHORT CIRCUIT EYES:

Eyes Open	(Left, Right, Up, down, Mid-line)
Eyes Closed	(Left, Right, Up, Down, Mid-line)
Eyes Open	(Near, Arms' length, Far)
Eyes back/forth 20 times	

SHORT-CIRCUIT: EYE TEST

DEFINITION

A test to identify movements and focal functions of the eye that produce stress reactions in the body.

TEST

1. MID-LINE: Have the person look straight ahead and TEST the dominant arm in both contraction and extension. Now have the person close the eyes and test again.

2. RIGHT/LEFT/UP/DOWN: Have the person open the eyes and look to the RIGHT as far as possible without moving the head and TEST. Repeat the procedure with the eyes looking to the LEFT as far as possible without moving the head and TEST. Repeat, looking UP. Repeat, looking DOWN. Finally, test all four eye positions WITH THE EYES CLOSED.

3. NEAR/FAR FOCUS: Have the person open the eyes. Hold a pen or, better, a pen-light, a foot in front of the eyes and TEST. Now move the pen or light out to arms-length and TEST.

4. BACK AND FORTH 20 TIMES: Move the pen or light back and forth in front of the eyes 20 times. When finished, TEST. (This is the equivalent of reading approximately half an hour.)

SHORT-CIRCUITED EYE TEST

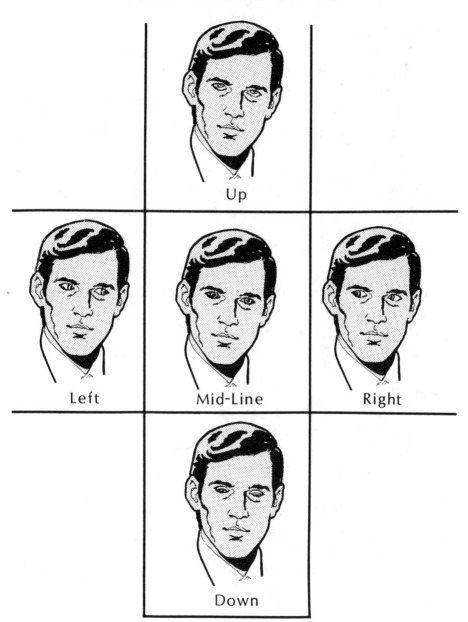

Up

Left

Mid-Line

Right

Down

Note all indicator changes, in both contraction and extension, on the examination form. Any indicator change = "short-circuited" eyes.

EXPLANATION

DOMINANT BRAIN'S CIA is committed to interpreting our overt behavior as well as our more covert emotional responses; it constructs theories to justify why these behaviors occur, and does so because of the brain's need to maintain consistency for all behavior. This special capacity reveals how important what we do/don't do is when it comes to our self-image (a "theory") and our self-esteem (another "theory"). So, when we don't read well, we find justifications for it.

True, the act of reading itself can weaken eye muscles due to the continued back and forth motion involved. Also true that fatigue, poor lighting, weak eye muscles and stress are some of the surface factors which contribute to reading "blank outs" or inhibited vision. But the truth also goes much deeper than any present-time surface factor. What about emotional stressors that locked into the system at the time we learned to read? How about all the times our little peers made fun of our slowness, or "dumbness" or general not-all-rightness in school? Or the teachers and parents who shamed and blamed us for not reading as well as they thought we should?

Maybe, due to specific emotional stressors, we found that the best justification for NOT reading was a physical condition that made reading difficult. What better and more creative way to achieve that limitation than by a SUBCONSCIOUS short-circuit of the eyes? Or to create a mid-line blind-spot? Not only would that create a genuine physical problem under stress, but there'd be no real way to blame you, since the condition probably could NOT be clinically diagnosed as to CAUSE.

So whether you like it or not, if as a child you were "slow" learning to read, chances are good you've continued that pattern into adult life to reinforce the justification of your self-image as a child. It may not sound useful, profitable, positive or productive - and from an objective view, it's not. But no one ever accused the CIA of being objective.

Correction on page   8-13

SHORT-CIRCUIT: EAR TEST

DEFINITION

A test which indicates that verbal information is not being comprehended easily under stress.

TEST

Have the person turn the head to the RIGHT. Test in contraction and extension. Repeat the procedure with your testee's head turned to the LEFT. An indicator change in either direction, or both, ears are "short-circuited."

EXPLANATION

Remember that the left ear goes to the right hemisphere and the right ear to the left hemisphere.

Think of an infant lying quietly contented after finishing its bottle. In the few minutes before it lapses into sleep the baby gurgles, babbles, and emits primal speech patterns while turning its head and eyes and stretching its arms toward a sound or a quick movement. At a later age it may point or look at the object, and by age two it may even name it. In any case, "naming" is preceded by babbling and a primal motor response, which in 80 per cent of the cases is to the right. From this, Marcel Kinsbourne speculates that the motor pattern responsible for early language (a rightward turning movement controlled by the left hemisphere) may be responsible for the better development of language in the left side of the brain. In other words, language is an expression of motor behavior, and the two of them can be expected to be closely linked.

Studies on the sending of separate messages to each ear for the purpose of measuring which ear is superior for different sounds - shows a right-ear superiority for sound in children five weeks of age. In the case of heard speech, infants as young as 24 hours demonstrate electrical responses that can be recorded from the speech processing areas in the left hemisphere. With non-speech sounds, the activity is recorded in the right hemisphere.

One of the ways researchers detect which brain hemisphere is most involved in speech and other functions in normal people is having them listen to two different words coming to the two ears at the same time. When several word pairs are given in a row, people are unable to report them all, and most right-handers prefer to report more accurately words given to their right ear. This seems to be related to the fact that signals from the right ear, although sent to both hemispheres, are preferentially sent to the left hemisphere, which controls speech. People who have speech represented in the right hemisphere, a very unusual occurrence even in left-handed people, more accurately report what their left ears hear.

So what about the left-ear (right hemisphere)? Music is its preferred auditory signal.

Well, that's the researchers' read-out. Let's look at the situation from a symbolic point of view. Think of the bottom-line essence of each brain hemisphere's PURPOSE.

DOMINANT wants control, safety and survival with as little fear, pain or fear of pain as possible. And threat in the moment is likely to produce stress - and stress = blind-spots. Being shouted at, hearing a hateful or fear-producing tone of voice, listening to "what you don't want to hear," or not hearing what you want to hear, these are all stressors. Short-circuiting an ear or ears in the moment is exactly like going deaf on cue. If it promotes survival of Belief System self-image, DOMINANT will provide that service <u>automatically</u>.

And what do you suppose would short-circuit ALTERNATE's ear? More than likely, it's DOMINANT <u>denying</u> the creative images coming through, the images that are foreign (therefore threatening) to CIA survival. Or possibly, it's a form of self-denial of one's own creativity. Think about it.

Correction on page 8-14

FIXATION TEST

DEFINITION

A test to determine the effect of stress on structural and endocrine activity, particularly those glands which are light sensitive.

TEST

Hold a piece of BLACK paper three to four inches in front of the person's eyes. While your testee looks at the color black, test the indicator muscle in both contraction and extension.

EXPLANATION

Since the body works as a total "whole," each of its component systems affects the whole system. And since awareness extends beyond the skin, environmental stimuli that affects one body system affects them all to some degree. Everyone's aware of how air quality can throw the human system out of whack. But have you considered the effect of LIGHT?

LIGHT affects more than the visual process (which effects everything else). Conditions of light AND DARK have a direct effect upon the endocrine system, particularly the pituitary and pineal glands.

Hormones secreted by the endocrine system influence both growth and function of the body through their effect on nerves and organs. The glandular network has key centers throughout the body, ranging from the pituitary and pineal, which are structural extensions of the brain itself, to ovaries and testes in the lower torso. Yet the "master gland," the pituitary, controls the rest of the system.

The pituitary is an extension of both brain and brainstem. You'll find it beneath the hemispheres and forward of the brainstem just over the roof of the mouth in line with the bridge of the nose. It possesses special cells that act as transducers to convert electrical signals into hormonal signals from many areas of the brain into the hormonal signals that activate the rest of the endocrine system.

It also teams with the reticular formation and hypothalamus and pituitary to form a combination which might be called the "stress-reaction" programming center for the whole body. The reticular formation (at the top of the brain stem) sums up the over-all nervous activity of the body. Its neurons respond to stimulation of touch receptors, sound reception in the ear, light receptors in the eye and chemical receptors in the stomach. The hypothalamus (above the reticular formation) has to do with <u>instinctive</u> response to anti-survival stimuli.

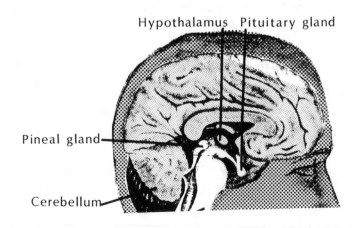

Hypothalamus Pituitary gland

Pineal gland

Cerebellum

Another light sensitive/receptive gland, the pineal gland is to the posterior brainstem what the pituitary is to the anterior brainstem - a natural extension of both brain and brainstem. Its name comes from its pine-cone shape. Smaller than the pituitary, the pineal has a wealth of nerve connections to the retina of the eye. Its cellular function combines the properties of nerve cells and epithelial cells (those cells which cover internal and external body surfaces).

The pineal also participates in childhood growth and, to some degree, sexuality. Not so strangely (when you consider the stressors of childhood learning), this gland starts to atrophy about the same time a child enters school (age 5 to 6), the same ages that (for most of us) "the light of learning" goes off and the darkness of "dyslexia" begins. By adulthood, the pineal has atrophied to slightly less than 1/3 of its original mass in the majority of human beings.

A REMINDER: Light lives within as well as coming from outside. The flash of light perceived when CAT is stimulated attests to this. So does the pupil's contraction or dilation due to emotion once the eye has adjusted to available outer light.

Also, to most of us humans, DARKNESS equates with increased tension more often than not. The absence of light makes it difficult to perceive with our primary visual sense, and that puts us at a disadvantage. Few movie horror stories are set in broad daylight. Just so in the mind. The most painful of experiences have such descriptive phrases attached to them as "that dark period of my life," or "a black mood," or "I'm completely in the dark as to what happened," or "that's a deep dark secret" And when we're confronted with shock or pain that's too intense to be dealt with, what takes place? We go "black out," go unconscious - another descent into darkness. And then, the ultimate: "the valley of the shadow." Death and darkness are inextricably paired. The light has gone out, permanently.

A preview of coming attractions: the correction for "fixation" is LIGHT.

What's interesting is that, over a 24 hour period, the production of stress hormones (ACTH) is closely linked with the light and dark cycle and the secretion varies considerably, reaching its lowest ebb toward the end of the dark period.

Occasional sharp, bright flashes of light will stimulate an entire train of brain waves, having almost the frequency of the Alpha rhythm. J.S. Barlow at MIT found that the sudden discharge of large number of neurons in the visual cortex produced by the bright flash of light was able to put the entire system into oscillation.

Fixation means "a fixed, immobilized state," among many other definitions. Recall that the eyes go functionally blind unless stimulated by motion. (A good example: stare at something long enough and you won't see it or anything else after awhile.)

Learning to read can be so traumatic under stressful circumstance that the child does just that, stares at one word, or even a letter of the alphabet, until a blindness to that word or letter takes place in the neurological system.

When the eye becomes frozen on an object through fear, pain or fear of pain, all the systems of the body freeze, too. The result is what we call fixation - darkness has replaced the light.

Correction on page 8-27

CROSS-PATTERNING	OK	NO Cont.	OK	NO Exten.
X (should test strong)	OK	NO Cont.	OK	NO Exten.
II (should test weak)	OK	NO Cont.	OK	NO Exten.

CROSS-PATTERNING

DEFINITION
A test to determine whether the neurological flow pattern between brain hemispheres is blocked.

TEST
You'll be testing three indicators during this procedure, so be sure they're Clear Circuits. Include quadriceps among them. As always in this examination, be sure to test in both contraction and extension.

FOR BODY COORDINATION
Have the person march in place using opposite arms and legs with the hands swinging across the mid-line. Then RETEST the muscles. There should be no indicator change. Record the results on the examination form.

Now have the person march in place using the same arm and leg. Then RETEST the muscles. The indicator should not hold strong. Make the appropriate notation.

FOR VISUAL PERCEPTION
Draw a large X on a flipchart, chalkboard or piece of paper. Have the person look at the X and TEST (use only one indicator muscle this time). There should be no indicator change.

Draw two parallel vertical lines beside the X. Have the person look at the vertical parallel lines and TEST. This should produce an indicator change.

If a person's indicator holds strong on both pairs of BOTH tests, do the correction regardless. After correction, the indicator should change as indicated above. If the person tests strong on both, there may be a problem in brain dominance, each hemisphere "competing" for control. Whichever brain is functioning - "turned on" - the other brain hemisphere should follow or support.

EXPLANATION

Among the most complex functions of the nervous system, the initiation and control of locomotion require the services of major portions of the brain. The body supports itself against gravity, maintains equilibrium, the direction of movement of the limbs must be guided, etc., etc. And since all movement involves "going toward or away" from a desired or distressful object, the eyes participate as does practically every other sense perception.

In the fetus, the earliest part of the brain to function is responsible for co-coordination and begins activity before the 16th week. While fetal development continues, the body works from the inside out and the outside in to provide adequate stimulation for this area of the brain. Interestingly, movement in the womb world tends to be ipsilateral - same arm/same leg, and the child is born with that same tendency. The reason? Researchers haven't investigated the "why," but for suppositional purposes, it might follow that since both brains have equal dominance in the infant, it's natural that whichever brain is "on" directs motion from its side of the body.

After birth, this pattern continues through various stages of body activity - first reaching and stretching, then from ipsilateral movements to cross-patterning (presumably, as brain dominance begins to manifest). Cross-patterning demonstrates the intrinsic cooperation and balance between brain hemispheres, and this ipsilateral-to-cross-patterning transfer of motion is the proof of that equality.

Should a child NOT go through this transfer to cross-patterning, real problems in coordination - mental and physical - may develop. Certainly, it would seem to be a dyslexic condition and/or <u>result</u> in a dyslexic condition. Those children who never crawled, but scooted on their seats until they started walking benefit greatly from cross-patterning exercises.

A young boy, age 7, came to us with a real problem in coordination. He'd been born with extreme pronation of the feet for which his doctor prescribed that he wear a bar brace to straighten them out. At age 2, he broke both legs. By the time we saw him, he had real difficulty skipping, running or walking a straight line. Through ONE BRAIN corrections with the emphasis on cross-patterning (and daily cross-patterning practice), his coordination increased 100-fold within a single month.

WHEN "X" AND PARALLEL LINES BOTH HOLD STRONG, you're dealing with a person whose Dominant/CIA puts a very high priority on <u>control.</u> This need for control characterizes everything about that individual. When you "have to be right," Dominant over-rides Alternate completely. Of course both X and parallel lines hold strong, until doing the correction finally reveals the true pattern - or, more accurately, <u>releases</u> the true pattern.

For such a person, this RELEASE may constitute the most important correction of any in ONE BRAIN's arsenal of skills.

Correction on page 8-5

HYOID TESTING

DEFINITION

A test of the hyoid system to determine current stress as related to dyslexic speech function.

TEST

<u>Gently</u> wiggle the hyoid area back and forth and TEST.   If the hyoid system is OK there will be no indicator change in either contraction or extension.

EXPLANATION

Located beneath the chin in the upper part of the neck, the hyoid is a free-floating bone shaped like a horseshoe and serves as the fixative point for the assessory muscles involved with chewing and speaking since these muscles also include the tongue. (For being such a small bone, it's amazing that 10 different muscles attach to it.)

For those who want to know, the muscles are:

Genioglossus, which protrudes and retracts the tongue.

Hyoglossus, which depresses the tongue and draws the sides down.

Geniohyoid, which draws the hyoid bone forward.

Mylohyoid, which forms the floor of the mouth and elevates the floor of the mouth and tongue.

Stylohyoid, which elevates and retracts the hyoid bone.

Digastric, which elevates the hyoid bone and lowers the jaw.

Thyrohyoid, which raises and changes form of larynx.

Omohyoid, which depresses the hyoid bone.

Sternohyoid, which depresses the hyoid bone and the larynx.

Infrahyoid, which can either depress the hyoid bone and larynx, or fix the hyoid bone so it cannot be elevated.

Obviously, this hyoidal area has a lot to do with speech and the stress and tension related to the consequences of both what we say and what we do NOT say. If such consequences have produced intense emotional trauma, an indicator change when testing the hyoid gives you a very specific clue as to the probable cause of a given dyslexic pattern.

Correction on page 8/2

TRANSVERSE FLOW TEST

DEFINITION
A test to determine if the energy extending from the physical body causes stress when disturbed.

TEST
Make a rapid pass up and down the body in a waving motion and TEST.

EXPLANATION
Energy emanates from our bodies. We can actually measure, photograph and feel this energy. More: it is constantly in motion, and that motion circles in a "Figure 8" pattern, crossing and re-crossing the mid-line, ever rebalancing itself through motion.

This flow passes over the major parts, torso, crossing the mid-line from the shoulder to the opposite hip; the legs, from the hip to the opposite foot, etc. The flow is also within every joint including joints of the fingers and toes, as well as over the head and under the bottom of the feet. And these flows reflect the electrical activity of individual and group cellular purpose.

Our bodies are electrically motivated machines which stimulate life through motion. So within cells, moving outward towards joints, to large portions of the body parts, this electrical energy expands until the entire body becomes encased - and, in that sense, protected. It's our own individual "force field," from an energy point of view.

As long as it's in a state of balanced transition, we're not aware of it and we "feel good." But when the balanced flow is blocked at some point (or within one of its component systems) we're aware of not feeling "quite right."

An indicator change in response to this test = a shock reaction when the person's protective energy-field is arbitrarily invaded.

Correction on page 8-2

NUTRITION/GENETIC TEST

DEFINITION

A test to identify current nutritional imbalances affecting the DNA/RNA needs of the individual system.

TEST

Touch the person's glabella with the tips of two fingers and TEST.

Glabella

EXPLANATION

The gene is the basic unit of heredity, and the principle working part of the gene is a gigantic molecule of deoxyribonucleic acid - DNA for short. DNA carries the whole genetic blueprint of the individual, incorporating it harmoniously into ever cell. The DNA molecules act as templates for the formation of ribonucleic acid or RNA. RNA has the power to reduce large protein molecules into the appropriate size to enter a given cell's membrane in order to "feed" it properly.

An easy way of looking at the duties of DNA/RNA: DNA is the blue print and RNA the engineer that makes duplication of that blueprint possible.

Obviously each of us needs proper nutrition. But keep in mind that "proper nutrition" for one genetic structure may not serve as well for another genetic structure. Nutrition is strictly an individual matter. Basic ground rules apply in general; specifics may need identification - which can be identified using appropriate muscle tests. And that's exactly what you may find yourself doing, should this category come up as a correction priority.

TOUCHING THE GLABELLA ALERTS THE PITUITARY, the master gland which harmonizes the chemical process/needs of the entire body in consonance with the genetic integrity of the individual. In effect, you're giving the pituitary the opportunity to tell you something of extreme importance.

Researchers believe the RNA/DNA balance has a major influence on memory and thus may be a major factor in dyslexic dysfunction. In experimenting with memory traces there's a strong indication that neuronal activity (incoming thought stimulates neuronal cells connected in reverberating circuits) increases the amount of RNA in the nerve cells. In turn, this promotes better over-all cell function.

Correction on page 8-25

COMMON INTEGRATIVE AREA (CIA) TEST

DEFINITION

To test to determine the degree of dominant hemisphere's forebrain/backbrain integration.

TEST

Tap the area behind the ear and above the mastoid process on the dominant side of the brain with all four fingers, then continue touch-contact with that area, and TEST. If the indicator changes, this means that backbrain/CIA is blocking out new input and CAT input, thereby denying CHOICE in the moment.

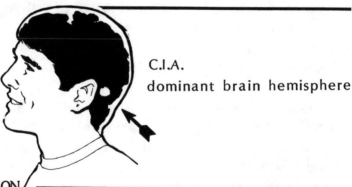

C.I.A.
dominant brain hemisphere

EXPLANATION

When under stress the CIA locks-on its survival mode. This means your testee has a pattern of reacting to stress based on old, and probably negative, backbrain experience. Control is a real issue with this person, even when feeling confused and mentally inept.

THE SAME LOCATION ON THE ALTERNATE BRAIN HEMISPHERE, if tested, may produce an indicator change. If it does, do not assume the dominant hemisphere is on the right. Research from the 1960s on verifies that the Dominant brain is USUALLY on the left side, even in people who are left handed.

Remember the NATURE of Alternate Brain's function. It's job description includes elements not found in Dominant's job description and vice versa. Still, this same location in the Alternate hemisphere must serve a "similar" purpose - one that reflects the holographic essence of Alternate's perception - and the multi-dimensional non-verbal language appropriate to that perception.

For further information on this interesting insight, see our STRUCTURAL NEUROLOGY. For right now, simply do the CIA test on the Dominant side only.

Correction on page 8/27.

EMOTIONAL STRESS STATEMENT _____
Positive statement	OK NO Cont.	OK NO Exten.
Negative statement	OK NO Cont.	OK NO Exten.

EMOTIONAL STRESS DEFUSION TESTS

DEFINITION

A test to determine the emotional stress factor in attitudes affecting perception in right/left brain hemispheres.

TEST

Have your testee identify the primary area of concern. Then use the following formula to make a positive and negative statement of the issue. Test both statements in both contraction and extension and note the results. The formula: "I want and trust my ability to/I do not want and do not trust my ability to." For example:

"I want and trust my ability to read well!"

"I do not want and do not trust my ability to read well!"

or . . .

"I want and trust my ability to do math well!"

"I do not want and do not trust my ability to do math well!"

or . . .

"I want and trust my ability to lose weight!"

"I do not want and do not trust my ability to lose weight!"

or . . .

"I want and trust my ability to take examinations successfully!"

"I do not want and do not trust my ability to take examinations successfully!"

NEGATIVE EMOTIONAL CHARGE ON THE ISSUE

Identify the **% of Negative Emotional Charge** on the issue (and/or <u>any</u> major issue that comes up in a defusion!). Make note of it on the examination form.

EXPLANATION

In the correction procedures you'll notice that we bring energy to the frontal area of the brain to defuse <u>present time</u> stressors, and to both frontal and occipital areas for <u>past</u> time stressors.

In the frontal lobes, CAT processes thoughts free of emotional impact. In the occipital lobes, the Primary Visual Area serves as the primary perceptive trigger for memories of past experience. CAT has only <u>short term memory</u> since its focus is strictly the moment, right now in present time.

What we choose to consider IN THE MOMENT has very little effect on how <u>memory</u> compels us to react. Years of programming take their toll. So if, in present time/right now, we choose to WANT something, that want has very little to do with whether we get it or not. Backbrain memory "knows the truth," and we end up acting as we have in the past. (Which explains why the "affirmation" approach so rarely works for most people.) The CIA disagrees with CAT any time <u>change</u> of self-image, attitude or performance is at issue because **the CIA equates change with fear, pain or fear of pain.**

Naturally, you'll find indicator disagreement on the above statements. No surprise there. Yet after you complete the correction procedures and retest, you'll find that the indicator holds strong for both positive and negative statements. That's exactly what you WANT to have happen. When both fore and backbrain respond <u>without stress,</u> the person has reached the point of real CHOICE in present time. Now there's no subconscious subtext to undermine the achievement of a desired positive.

As long as the person continues choosing to choose the <u>positive</u> behavior, it will manifest as a matter of course. Not that the road ahead won't be bumpy, but now at least the journey can begin. CIA's fear of change is no longer the determining factor in that area of behavior.

Correction on page 8/18

```
┌─────────────────────────────────────────────────────┐
│                                                     │
│        ISOLATING CORRECTION PRIORITIES              │
│                                                     │
│  This is what you need to know to identify the key areas of │
│  outage involved with dyslexic defusion.            │
│                                                     │
│  These two procedures have immense value - so much value, │
│  in fact, that we're giving them this special section for special │
│  emphasis.                                          │
│                                                     │
└─────────────────────────────────────────────────────┘
```

DIGITAL DETERMINATION

DEFINITION

A system which uses the thumb in opposition to each of the four fingers in turn to identify major categories of outage in the body.

TEST

Use a Clear Circuit indicator muscle, be sure the person isn't switched and that the Central/Governing meridians are in good shape.

Test on the Dominant side, positioning the muscle in contraction. Have the person you're testing place index finger to thumb and TEST. Then repeat with the remaining fingers, testing each in turn.

Should no indicator change take place, RETEST IN EXTENSION. If there's still no change, test the Alternate side of the body - first in contraction, then in extension if necessary to produce results or verify there is no change.

An indicator change when the index finger touches the thumb means that the STRUCTURAL category needs attention.

An indicator change when the middle finger touches the thumb means that NUTRITIONAL/GENETIC category needs attention.

An indicator change when the ring finger touches the thumb means that the EMOTIONAL category needs attention.

An indicator change when the little finger touches the thumb means that the ELECTRICAL category needs attention.

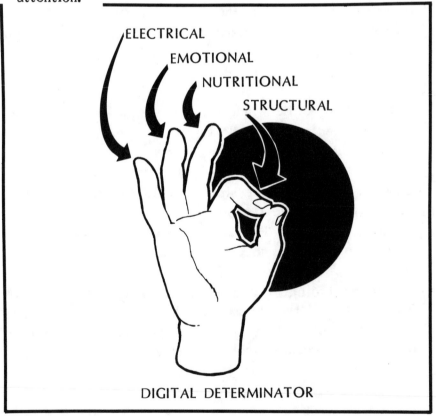

ELECTRICAL
EMOTIONAL
NUTRITIONAL
STRUCTURAL

DIGITAL DETERMINATOR

EXPLANATION

The THUMB represents a <u>neutral</u> energy flow; the fingers are polarized, positive and negative, as are the two sides of the body. For example: The index finger of the right hand is positive while the index finger of the left hand is negative; the middle finger of the right hand is negative while the left's is positive; right's ring finger is positive, left's is negative; little finger RIGHT is negative, little finger LEFT is positive.

The reason you're testing Dominant's DIGITAL DETERMINATORS? According to Dr. A. R. Mauldin, the dominant brain processes 85% of digital function, the alternate only 15%.

For thousands of years, finger positions have been used to balance energy in the body. And different finger positions appear to create different effects, both symbolically and physically, in different cultures. For examples, just recall the religious statuary of Egypt, Greece, China, and India - not to mention the various yoga positions.

REACTIVE MUSCLES INDICATOR

DEFINITION

A "blanket" test to discover whether an energy blockage involves a pattern of muscular reaction throughout the body.

TEST

Hold your hand an inch and a half over the sagittal suture and TEST. A muscle change indicates the involvement of reactive muscles.

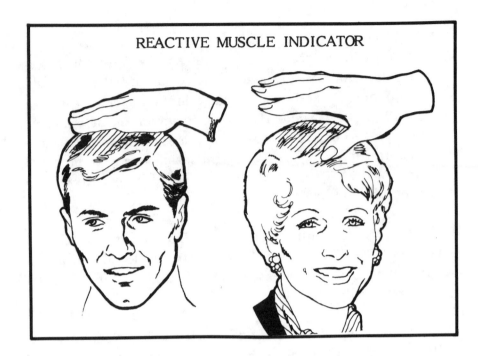

REACTIVE MUSCLE INDICATOR

EXPLANATION

The sagittal suture articulates the parietal skull plates directly over the fissure which separates the brain hemispheres. Below the sagittal suture we find the motor areas of the parietal/frontal brain lobes and, beneath these, the cerebellum - that amazing computer which integrates all muscular expression of the body. More: the pineal gland, an extension of the brain stem, nestles beneath the cerebellum's right and left lobes.

As mentioned earlier, the pineal is to the backbrain what the pituitary is to the forebrain, its "third eye" in effect. Sightless cave salamandars "see" in total darkness due to the light receptivity of the pineal. An open sagittal suture provides the "light source."

Reactive muscles = all muscles in motion at a moment of physical or emotional trauma. Since any trauma involves what we saw and heard (or both) at "the moment of impact," most often the key trigger to that reactive pattern is either the <u>eye position or the ear on the side that "heard,</u> or both.

The moment of impact weakens the muscles in motion, causing other muscles to try harder as part of a chain reaction effect throughout the body, beginning with the neck (its position when we "saw it coming" - or heard the sounds), then running down the torso, arms and legs. The effect? Continued muscular imbalance which will continue until the causal stressor receives defusion.

Such imbalances can produce all kinds of physical symptoms - neck and back pain, "strained" muscles in any part of the body and even internal complaints having to do with digestion, elimination and reproductive function.

AGE RECESSION

DEFINITION

A test to identify the age at which specific physical, emotional or spiritual trauma resulted in a learning dysfunction. Note: the time span to be covered during Age Recession is "from present time, right now, to conception."

We're not doing age regression, please note. Webster defines a "recess" as "a secluded, withdrawn or inner place: such as a subterranean recess, or the recesses of the subconscious." Age Recession takes us back to those inner places of the subconscious and the specific times when Negative Emotional Charge blocked our perception.

TEST

1. In present time, establish the issue and find its **% of Negative Emotional Charge.** Having done so, go through the Digital/Reactive Determinators and make any corrections until all Digital positions hold strong.

2. Now go back from present time in increments of 10 years, testing each in turn. If the person's 44 say, "From present time, right now," and TEST. "Age 44," and TEST. "From 44 to 40," and TEST. "From 40 to 30," and TEST. "From 30 to 20," and TEST. "From 20 to 10," and TEST. "From 10 to birth," and TEST. "From birth to conception," and TEST.

3. When the indicator changes, go backwards from the highest number, one year at a time. For example, say, "10," and TEST. "9," and TEST. "8," and TEST. "7," and TEST. "6," and TEST. The indicator will again change at the specific age involved.

If the indicator changes on more than one year, the person has SWITCHED. Go through the un-switching correction, and begin again from the highest number. "10," and TEST. "9," and TEST, etc.

4. Now find out the **% of Negative Emotional Charge** on the issue at that age, then do the Digitals. Correct any "outs" until all hold strong and % of Negative Emotional Charge is 0.

In Age Recession don't anticipate that you'll find the same "outs" identified during the examination - or what was "out" in present time. During Age Recession, your testee responds according to past time, and "what's out" may be something else entirely. With different neurons turned on, you'll get different answers from the body.

5. It's <u>vital</u> to make sure that everything is cleared up before you move on. Retest using Digital/Reactive Determinators until they all hold strong. When they do, tell the person to "Hold strong" and retest the age which caused the indicator change. If the indicator changes when you say the age and TEST, there's more work to be done. Repeat Digital/Reactive Determinators until ALL hold strong.

6. When there is no more to be done at this age, bring the person BACK TO PRESENT TIME muscle testing in increments of 10. Tell the person to "Hold strong," restate the age, "6" and TEST. "From 6 to 10," and TEST. "From 10 to 20," and TEST. "From 20 to 30," and TEST. "From 30 to 40," and TEST. "From 40 to present time, right now," and TEST.

This return muscle test is important because it anchors the body. Always bring the person back to "present time, right now" before further Age Recession, since the ages may not be clearly sequential. For instance, the next time, the indicator might change at age 35, the next time at 4, then at 12, finally at 3 months in the womb. Complete each cycle by coming back "to present time, right now." The body will give you the priorities to work on in the correct order. You may even bypass ages when your testee knows a related traumatic experience took place, but trust the body. When those experiences are ready to be defused, they will show up. And you'll find that the person goes through them easily without adding further trauma to the system. Honor the person and honor the procedure and you'll get beautiful results.

7.   Now that you've returned to "present time, right now," go through the Digital/Reactive Determinators again. Make any corrections that show up as a result of Age Recession.

8.   Continue the process until you get a hold-strong test from conception to "present time, right now" - with 0% Negative Emotional Charge on the issue and all Digital positions holding-strong as well. In the process, you've defused more dyslexic blindspots than you or your testee realize. When you retest examination "outs," you'll be amazed at the results.

NOTE: Should you or your testee not have time to complete the whole process during one session, you can stop once you've brought the person back to "present time, right now" and all Determinators hold strong. Never leave a person in a past time-frame - it creates a spacey, disconnected feeling that promotes temporary confusion and/or disorientation.

EXPLANATION

It's no secret that memory is recorded in many parts of the brain. Both right and left hemispheres store specific kinds (and portions) of any given memory. In addition, key spinal centers retain patterns of programmed function; so do the organs of the body. That even the smallest cellular unit can reproduce its duplicate indicates that a memory consciousness exists within that cell. Similarly, a surgically transplanted muscle that replaces another muscle's function, will operate in a "dyslexic" manner until consciously "re-taught."

There's no separation between the experience of the central nervous system and the function of memory in every cell of the body. The experience of the past has been fixed and retained by the neurons firing at that precise moment. Every muscle, nerve, and tissue participating in that experience has been affected and will "remember" in its own fashion.

Wilder Penfield represents many neurological researchers in his conclusion the record of all we have experienced remains in the central nervous system. Nothing is forgotten.

In reference to his research with the brain's temporal lobe, Penfield writes: "Since the electrode may activate a random sample of this strip from the distant past, and since the most unimportant and completely forgotten periods of time may appear in this sampling, it seems that it really does include all the periods of each individual's waking conscious life . . . the stream of consciousness flows inexorably onward (as described in the words of William James), but unlike a river it leaves behind a permanent record that seems to be complete for the waking moments of a man's life - a record that runs, no doubt, like a thread along a pathway of ganglionic and synaptic facilitations in the brain."

Peter Nathan, research neurologist at the National Hospital for Nervous Diseases, London wrote: "At one time I was studying the problems of the relief of pain sometimes experienced by patients after amputations of limbs. One of these patients was a young man, who had lost his leg during the Korean War. During the course of a day, I carried out various procedures to the stump of his lower limb, many of which were painful and all of which had the effect of sending into the spinal cord a barrage of nerve impulses from that limb."

"On the night after these tests, the patient suddenly awakened from sleep with severe pain in his absent leg. He immediately knew what his pain was. For five years previously, before he had his leg amputated, he had fallen playing ice hockey and had the outside of his leg cut open by a skate. On the present night he re-experienced the identical sensations in his phantom leg that he had had at that time. It was not that he remembered having had this injury; he felt all the sensations again in his absent leg that he had previously felt. The presence of some change was shown by stimulating the same neurons again on another occasion, several years later."

During psychotherapy, memories from the past roll up, though they had not been recalled previously. Often they return to possess us again with the same intensity of emotion and the adult will become the child, raging away at how his parents "are" treating him. It makes us wonder how much we really ever forget.

One last example - from the research of Dr. Robert G. Health, head of the Tulane School of Medicine's Neurology/Psychiatry Department: when a person remembers past marijuana experiences, the same brain activity takes place as when actually smoking marijuna.

CORRECTIONS

We've listed the corrections according to DIGITAL Determination - beginning with ELECTRICAL (little finger to thumb), then EMOTIONAL (ring finger to thumb), next NUTRITION/GENETIC (long finger to thumb), STRUCTURAL (index finger to thumb), and REACTIVES (hand held over sagittal suture). For easy reference, we put the chapter/page number right after each correction category - such as Transverse Flow/5-30, Hyoid/5-28 - preceding each section.

ELECTRICAL CORRECTIONS

Transverse Flow/5-30   Short-Circuit: Eyes/5-12
Hyoid/5-28   Short-Circuit: Ears/5-16
Cross-Patterning/5-24   Alphabet/Counting/5-5
Reading Perception/5-5   Crossing the Mid-line/5-8

Keep in mind that the ELECTRICAL DETERMINATOR (little finger to thumb) has to do with mis-communication between the two brain hemispheres. Dominant has chosen not to honor the balancing messages that come from Alternate, and instead locks-on to control based on past experience and survival-patterns. The dyslexic blindspot here is basically a lack of awareness for positive input from within the WHOLENESS of self; a DENIAL of Alternate's imagistic prompting under stress which all too often involves a feeling of "Who am I really?"

TRANSVERSE FLOW

Touch the navel with two or more fingers of one hand. With your other hand, span the forehead, touching one frontal eminence with two fingers and the other frontal eminence with your thumb. Now HOLD your connection for a minute or so, and tell the person to BREATHE. All the 8's - even those in the knuckles and kneecaps - should be in balance. Make a rapid pass up and down the body in a waving motion, and RETEST. The indicator should hold strong. If it doesn't, simply repeat the correction, then retest.

HYOID

When you tested the person's hyoid, the indicator changed because one of the many muscles involved is over-energy/"too strong." To discover this, you'll "alert" each of the muscles in turn by touch, specifically by stroking them with two fingertips or your thumb. Stroking increases tension in an over-energy muscle which results in an indicator change.

NOTE: The hyoid bone is located above the thyroid cartilage (the so-called "Adam's apple"). In the following tests, keep this clearly in mind.

1) Start near the back of the ear and stroke forward underneath the jaw toward the chin and TEST. Now do the other side.

2) Stroke down the mid-line from the tip of the chin to the thyroid cartilage and TEST.

3) Stroke upward from the outer third of the right clavicle toward the hyoid bone and TEST. Repeat on the left side.

4) With your thumb on one side of the throat <u>above the thyroid cartilage</u> and your fingers on the other side, <u>gently</u> torque the hyoid process clockwise - this alerts the muscle on the left side - and TEST. Next, <u>gently</u> torque in a counter-clockwise direction - which alerts the muscle on the right - and TEST.

Now go to the spindle cells in the belly of those muscles which caused an indicator change and <u>gently</u> pinch once or twice to relax the muscle. Check to be sure the correction worked: <u>very gently,</u> wiggle the hyoid process back and forth again and TEST. The indicator muscle should now stay strong.

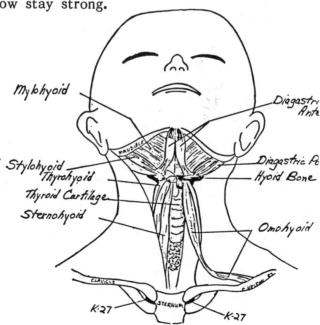

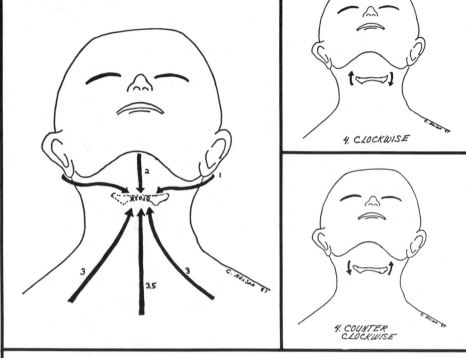

HYOID CORRECTION
Go to the stretched muscle and pinch once or twice to tone down the spindle cells.

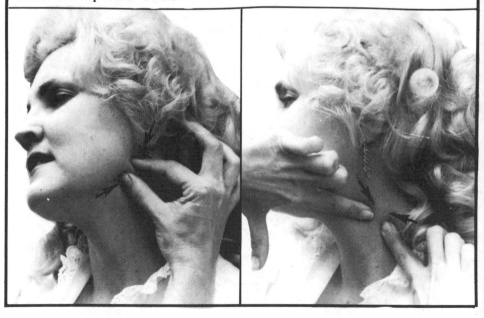

CROSS-PATTERNING

Use this correction - and also give it as a homework/reinforcement assignment - when the person's indicator holds strong on the ipsilateral exercise and/or when looking at the parallel lines.

1. Have the person do 6 or 7 repetitions of the cross-over exercise (opposite hand and leg) <u>alternating</u> it with the ipsilateral exercise (same side hand and leg). Repeat 4 or 5 times. Be sure to end with the person doing the cross-patterning. RETEST.

Now have the person look at the X and TEST. Then have the person look at the parallel lines and TEST. You should only get an indicator change on the parallel lines.

If the person has difficulty doing this cross-over exercise and/or the correction doesn't "take," have the person think of or look at an X <u>and Age Recess</u> until the indicator changes. Now repeat the correction exercise and RETEST. Repeat the procedure until the indicator holds strong on the cross-over pattern and changes on the ipsilateral.

Now have the person look at or visualize the X again and continue to Age Recess until you get another indicator change. Repeat the cross-over exercise/test procedure. Continue tracking back until the indicator holds strong whenever the person thinks of or looks at the X, and changes only on parallel lines. Once that's taken place, bring the person back to present time, repeat the exercise and RETEST to verify correction.

2. When the person's coordination improves to the point there's no problem doing the cross-over exercise, connect more of the brain into the circuit by doing the following. With the head kept straight forward, have your testee do the cross-over exercise while moving the eyes "all around the clock" - straight ahead, straight up, up right, side right, down right, straight down, down left, side left, up left, straight up, straight ahead, and so on. Now reverse the eye movements and go the opposite way while doing the cross-over exercise.

3. When the person can do both Steps 1 and 2 easily, involve even more neurons by adding the voice and the brain's LANGUAGE centers. Have the person recite the alphabet in concert with each eye movement. Or the person can speak the times table, or learn the spelling of words.

If your testee stutters or stammers, have the person SING the alphabet, times table or the spelling of words.

ASSIGN THESE CORRECTIONS AS TWICE-A-DAY HOMEWORK for people who want to improve their physical/mental coordination. That's right - the exercises have as positive an effect on the body as the brain. Do them daily - especially when stress hits the system. Using them at such times keeps the body balanced, the mind alert, and relieves much physical stress, fatigue and muscle soreness. Most of all, it helps us to maintain effectiveness "under fire."

These exercises are also invaluable to use as preparation BEFORE any stressful activity, physical or mental. And as a general "toner," do them morning and night.

HERE ARE SOME VARIATIONS ON THE THEME THAT MAKE THE EXERCISES MORE FUN. All of them begin in a standing position, and be sure you're using OPPOSITE arms and legs. Do 10 to 30 strokes in each of the following sequences, work within your own energy-range and keep it loose and easy. We think it's more fun to exercise with music - plus it gets the Alternate Brain involved. Up-beat up-tempos make you feel good.

SEQUENCES FOR THE EXERCISE

MARCH IN PLACE - raise opposite arm/leg at the same time.

TORSO TWIST - raise knee and touch it with opposite elbow.

FORWARD STRETCH - raise opposite arm/leg straight out to the front; reach forward and allow waist to bend. Bend the supporting leg if keeping it straight feels uncomfortable.

ARM/LEG LIFT - lift opposite arm/leg out to the side; keep leg as straight as possible.

BACK STRETCH - opposite arm/leg swing to the rear; keep leg as straight as possible.

READING PERCEPTION TEST

We want to impress you again that reading has to be one of the most intricate and complicated of all body activities. The most delicate of our muscles continually adjust to move the eyeballs back and forth, constant adjustments to the curvature of the lens keep the eyes focused while the pupil adjusts just as often to regulate the amount of light that enters the eye - and all this may take place in an environment of emotional stress. Should stress fixate the eye, we literally go blind to what's on the printed page. The eye can no longer make sense out of the minute differences in the shapes of the letters which must take place if we're to understand what we see.

If reading out loud, the vocal cords also come into play. In those who mentally "say" every word they read, the vocal cords are involved whether we know it or not. Plus, if what we read aloud is being judged as to effectiveness according to someone else's standards (or even our own), every word we read becomes a test, a stressor that blocks the natural flow of ions which transmit electro-chemical messages from brain to body.

These ion-messengers initiate the nerve impulses that move muscles by changing a muscle's energy from positive to negative and vice versa. This natural fluctuation can become blocked, and reading is a prime causor for such positive/negative energy blockage. For this reason, rebalancing the energy system becomes one of the most fundamental corrections.

Since the energy flows of the body are, in effect, controlled by the meridians, the primary correction works to release blockages in that amazing system and involves a master acupressure point that influences all of the body's meridians. This master acupressure point appears in the illustration. It's K27 (Kidney Meridian, the 27th acupressure point on that meridian).

TO CORRECT WHEN THE INDICATOR CHANGES ON READING ALOUD: Touch all four fingertips of one hand to the navel and with your other fingertips rub K27, first on the right, then on the left, WHILE the person moves the eyes "around the clock" and straight forward, simultaneously saying the alphabet aloud. (You're absolutely right - it's Step 2 of the cross-over exercise without involving the body.) Once you've finished both clockwise and counter-clockwise cycles, CHANGE HAND POSITIONS (read: "change polarities") and repeat the process. RETEST to verify the correction.

TO CORRECT WHEN THE INDICATOR CHANGES ON READING SILENTLY: Have the person read silently as you touch the navel and palpate right/left K27 WHILE the person reads silently. Change hands/polarity and repeat. RETEST to verify the correction.

ASSIGN WHICHEVER EXERCISE CORRECTS THE CONDITION AS HOMEWORK. Actually, you may be assigning both exercises more often than not. Have the person do it/them whenever there's a need to read extensively. And don't overlook it as a "toner" for yourself under the same circumstances.

BACK-UP MERIDIAN BALANCER FOR PEOPLE IN EXTREME STRESS: Called the COOK METHOD, after its discoverer, this is an excellent way to unblock meridians when a person's eyes show 2nd and 3rd Stage Stress. It has two parts.

PART ONE: In a sitting position, cross your left leg over your right knee, then place your right hand over the left ankle bone. (See illustration). TEST. If the indicator changes, reverse the pattern by putting the right foot over the left leg with the left hand covering the right ankle bone following the same instructions.

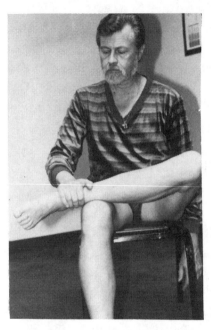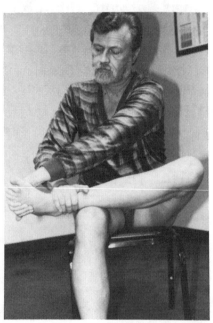

To complete the first part of the balancing, wrap your left hand around the ball of the foot so your fingers reach around the little toe to cover the top of the foot. Now, with the circuit complete, put your tongue to the roof of your mouth and BREATHE IN, then BREATHE OUT while you hold the tongue down. Repeat at least three times.

SECOND PART: Release the circuit, relax and sit in a normal position while you put your fingertips together and continue to BREATHE as above.

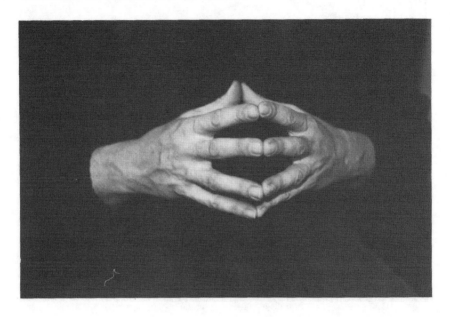

SHORT-CIRCUIT: EYES

Have the person look in the direction that caused an indicator change. If the change came while focusing near or far, put an object at that distance so the person can continue to focus on it while you make the correction. And you'll make this same correction for <u>each</u> eye position that caused an indicator change.

THE CORRECTION POINTS are located about an inch and a half right/left of the mid-line just above the occipital protuberance (see illustration). The indentations you'll find in these locations are the EYE POINTS. Rub the eye points while the person's eyes remain focused in the position (or at the distance) that caused a muscle change. RETEST to verify correction.

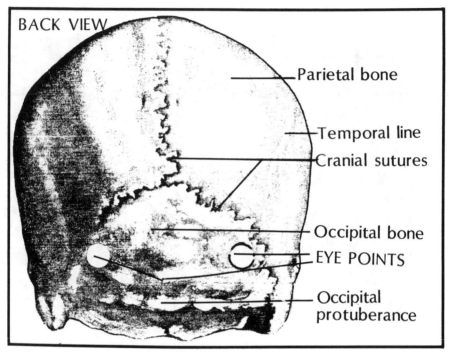

BACK VIEW

Parietal bone

Temporal line

Cranial sutures

Occipital bone

EYE POINTS

Occipital protuberance

SHORT-CIRCUIT: EARS

Interestingly, the upper half of the ears outer perimeter conforms to the shape of the skull and, in that sense, to the basic proportions of the hemisphere housed within. The symbolic implication of this correction is fascinating.

Pull and extend the outer perimeter (helix) of the ear that originally caused a muscle change. Do this gently in "rolling up and out direction", starting from the lobe and moving all the way around the ear to the anterior joining of the helix. RETEST to verify correction.

ALPHABET/COUNTING

You'll do the following for each letter/number that produced an indicator change.

FOR LETTERS OF THE ALPHABET: have the person join the hands in such a way that fingers and thumbs cross, leaving a triangular-ish opening over the thumbs through which to sight. Now have the person take a <u>broad stance,</u> feet well apart, and sight through that opening to <u>write the letter's lower case form</u> in the air, using whole body participation. Make the letter as BIG as possible, bending the knees to involve the maximum of large muscle movement. Extend to the right and left sides as far possible, too. Repeat at least three times.

Next, reduce the <u>scale and scope</u> of body involvement. Bring the legs to the regular standing position, sight through the hands' opening and repeat writing the letter's lower case form. Do this at least three times.

Last, reduce the scale even further - by increments. First, go to smaller movements. Then to regular piece of paper (using a pen or pencil), then to half of that. Last of all - and as important as any previous correction steps - have the person close eyes and repeat the process <u>in the mind.</u> RETEST to verify correction.

FOR NUMBERS: the process is the same. Have the person sight through the hands' opening, start big, reduce scope and scale of body involvement until he or she actually writes the number on paper. Again, closing eyes and repeating the process <u>mentally</u> puts the capper on this series of correction exercises. RETEST to verify correction.

CROSSING THE MID-LINE

Special education and vision training programs have used the following exercise for many years because it produces superior results. Doing it enables a person to cross the midline with continuous motion, which prevents a short-circuit of right brain energy. It also integrates activities which have been done ipsilaterally before. Since the figure used is the <u>symbol of infinity,</u> once again the implication speaks for itself.

USING THE INFINITY SYMBOL TO CROSS THE MIDLINE: have the person draw the symbol on a chalkboard or flip chart. Make the symbol as wide as space permits. (See illustration.) Use the Dominant hand for the first stage of this exercise. Start with an UPWARD motion to make the first circle, then down, around and up to make the second circle. Repeat 6 or 7 times, or until it becomes comfortable for the Dominant hand.

Do this a second time using the Alternate hand, then a third time using BOTH hands for the same number of repetitions.

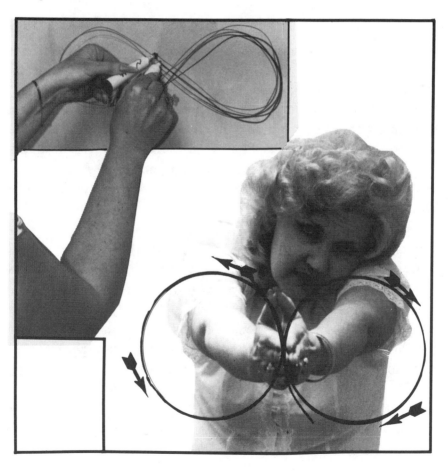

NOW REPEAT "IN THE AIR" A LA THE ALPHABET and/or COUNTING CORRECTION: have the person cross fingers and thumbs to form an arm's length sight. First, the broad stance/bent knee/whole body version. Second, the natural standing posture reduction in scope and scale. Third, the closed-eye mental version. RETEST to verify correction.

EMOTIONAL

Emotional Stress Statement/5-36

When ring finger to thumb produces an indicator change, your testee has blockages on the emotional level. Such blockages rarely have to do with right/left brain mis-communication. It's far more likely a clash of CIA and CAT on the Dominant hemisphere only. The problem is one of self-image and Belief System as they were formed at times of crisis in the past, and/or as they relate right now in present time to basically similar situations. The resultant blindspot takes expression of feelings such as "I'm not OK" - or "There's really something wrong with me."

Remember NOW results from THEN, so THEN always affects NOW - positively or negatively as we ALLOW. THEN problems key-in the same subconscious response to a consciously-perceived NOW problem. The only way to defuse THEN's effect (and CIA's lock-on) is to move the energy from backbrain to forebrain so that CAT's input can register in consciousness and make possible a positive CHOICE possible.

With BRAIN BASICS in mind, defusing emotional stress makes logical sense. It's simply a matter of centering energy in the part of the brain which produces the kind of mental activity that benefits you most. And how do you center energy in the brain? By sustained touch that draws vascular and cerebrospinal fluids to the area you're holding - due to the warming, magnetic energy of your fingers and/or hands.

There are three ONE BRAIN corrections for ESD (Emotional Stress Defusion): Frontal Holding for right now/present time stressors, Frontal/Occipital Holding for stressors from the past, and Body Scan - which we use to locate energy blockages in the body, either in the present or the past.

FOR PRESENT TIME STRESSORS: FRONTAL HOLDING
If touching ring finger to thumb produced an indicator change, as your testee to identify the probable present time stressor. With that situation, have the person close eyes and focus only on that stressor. Again TEST. If the indicator changes, proceed with the Frontal Holding ESD correction.

Touch one frontal eminence with two fingertips and the other with your thumb. Or you can cover the whole forehead with your hand. This draws exterior/interior circulation AWAY from Dominant's temporal lobe and centers brain activity under your touch. Keep your contact with the frontal eminences LIGHT, use just enough pressure to move the skin. Continue this connection for about a minute, reminding your testee to BREATHE at regular intervals.

Your job, during the time of holding, is to relax and focus on nothing but what you can discern through touch. Become aware of the frontal eminence <u>pulse</u> under your fingertips. Notice whether that pulse differs, right from left.

If you're using this skill for the first time, it's quite possible you may not sense any difference in the pulses right and left, or even any "pulse" at all. Not to worry! Given several sessions of Frontal Holding, you'll attune to that sensation as a matter of course. It's quite <u>real</u>. Just give yourself time and opportunity; the awareness will come.

Now you have the opportunity to assist your testee CONSCIOUSLY defuse the stressor. Here are some valuable "assists":

1. Ask the person to put the stressful situation back in mind. Have your testee to replay it <u>mentally, in silence,</u> and with as much detail as possible. Run it through from beginning to end - and take DEEP BREATH when the replay comes to the end.

The reason NOT to verbalize comes from brain basics. Speaking turns on the Language Centers and they're so intimately related to the CIA that you slow down the energy shift you want to create.

Once the DEEP BREATH alerts you that the replay's over, ask your testee to repeat the process twice more - and with each repetition SEE MORE, HEAR MORE, SENSE MORE DETAILS. The more details we see/sense during ESD the more we're defusing the impact of that total memory in EVERY center where its stored within the brain. Tell the person to signal replay-completion by a DEEP BREATH.

2. Ask, "Is there any skill or knowledge you could have used to change, improve, or make-right the situation? If you had it all to do over again, what would you do differently?" Now the person can verbalize, since the CIA has learned options other than knee-jerk emotional reversion and unproductive survival patterns. Once such an option comes to mind: have the person review the situation in silence one more time using the NEW OPTION and having the situation work out to positive advantage - and signal the end by a DEEP BREATH.

Why this step? Because in taking it, consciousness is being reprogrammed to respond differently in all future similar situations. Remember, the brain makes no distinction between real and/or imagined experience. A changed outcome, even if experienced in imagination, registers as actual and REAL. Not only have you defused this situation's emotional charge, but produced the good of the "lesson" the situation represents.

HOLD/TOUCH until your feel the pulses synchronize. Then have your testee "Take another deep breath." Reposition the indicator muscle, ask the person to put that stressor back in mind and RETEST to verify correction.

FOR PAST STRESSORS: FRONTAL/OCCIPITAL HOLDING

You'll use F/O Holding for all Age Recession outages that involve the Emotional Determinator. And, you may choose to use it to reinforce any Emotional correction that comes up in present time as the result of Age Recession.

With your testee standing, sitting or lying down (whichever position seems most appropriate), cover the frontal eminences with one hand and the Primary Visual Areas of both occipital lobes (the skull's occiput) with your other hand. Throughout F/O Holding, remind your testee to BREATHE.

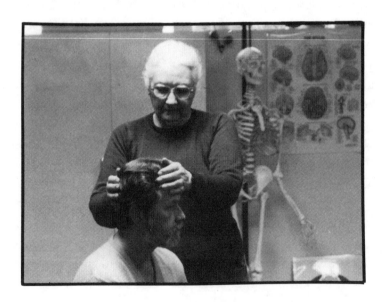

Also _synchronize_ your breathing with that person's. Put your whole attention on the process: ATTUNE!

During Age Recession, you'll want to have the person verbalize the situations that come up at different periods of time for the same reason mentioned in Frontal Holding - the more sense input you can create, the more memory neurons you defuse of negative emotion.

HOWEVER, your job has to do with reactivating sense input, not problem solving. Any "changed outcomes" must come from the individual, or you're just getting in the way. Stick to questions about what was seen, heard, or touched; what the temperature was, the time of day, the place where it happened, who was involved - questions which involve more and more details.

A SPONTANEOUS, DEEP BREATH/SIGH signals completion of a way-station along the path of any given Age Recession. But always RETEST to verify correction.

FOR USE IN PAST OR PRESENT TIME: THE BODY SCAN
A very revealing skill, the Body Scan alerts you and the testee to the location of blocked/locked energy that relates to a specific emotional stressor. Use a constant TEST with one hand while, with the other, you scan the body. Keep your "scanner" about an inch or two above/away from the body and begin with the head. Go over the head on one side of the body, over the ears and shoulders, down the side to the feet and up the other side. Next scan the mid-line, then down the front of one leg and up the front of the other. Do the same with the back, run a mid-line scan from the top of the head down the spine, then the back of the legs. TAKE NOTE OF THOSE AREAS OF THE BODY THAT PRODUCE AN INDICATOR CHANGE.

Indicator changes during body scan tell you that emotional defusion is not yet complete. To correct, use Frontal Holding while holding the area that caused an indicator change - and remember to have the person BREATHE!

The body-area that causes the indicator change gives extremely valuable information on how you can assist the defusion process.

If the area is the ears, you might ask: "Was there something you didn't want to hear?" If the eyes, "Was there something you didn't want to see?" If the throat, "Was there something you needed to say and didn't or couldn't?" Feet, "Was there something you wanted to run away from?" Hands, "Whom did you want to hit out at?" Shoulders, "Was there a responsibility you didn't want to shoulder?"

Ask for feedback, then interact as a good listener or "surrogate target" as appropriate. For instance, if something wasn't said, have the person say it to you now. Trust your intuition and imagination. And remember, just acknowledging the painful situation helps defuse it.

Again, while defusing with Body Scan, use Frontal Holding with one hand and touch the body-area that caused the indicator change. When you consider defusion complete, ask your testee to "take a deep breath." RETEST to verify correction.

NUTRITION/GENETIC

Nutrition/Genetic/5-32

If the indicator changes when you test with the middle finger touching the thumb means that the Nutrition/Genetic category causes stress. Generally speaking, this means that the body has an allergic response to specific foods, supplements or medication, based on that substance's adverse stimuli to the genetically determined needs of the body. The feeling this produces sums itself up as, "There's something wrong with my body, but I can't imagine what it is or why I have it."

Specifically, the glabella point relates to a need for additional DNA/RNA, a substance which helps in balancing both brain hemispheres. An indicator change in this category suggests the person could profitably add this supplement to the diet.

On the other hand, the body may be dehydrated and need water. A dehydrated system is a poor conductor of the electro-chemical nerve/muscle messages. Check this out, and if <u>a sip of water</u> held in the mouth while you test makes the muscle hold strong, have the person drink one or more glasses of water before proceeding. Having ingested the water, TEST the category again to verify correction.

As to specifics on "adverse stimuli," we go into detail on nutritional testing in the Advanced ONE BRAIN and STRUCTURAL NEUROLOGY manuals. For your purposes in Basic ONE BRAIN corrections, you might choose to suggest your testee check out the possibilities with the health authority of that person's preference.

Symbolically, the "Genetic" half of this category represents the basic structural formation of body/brain that came from Mommy and Daddy's chromosomatic contributions. Such being the case, Mommy and Daddy may be at issue when this category causes the indicator to change. Not necessarily Mommy and Daddy in the flesh - although very often that IS the case - but the genetic differences WITHIN the individual's structure which "pull in different directions," just as Mommy and Daddy pulled against each other when we were growing up. The person may be into resenting Mother's characteristics as they surface in self, or "the Daddy within" may be causing interference on the line. It's valuable and interesting to check out this aspect, too. Certainly, it gives you some vital clues in how to verbalize during the Age Recession defusion process, should Nutrition/Genetic surface as an important part of the picture.

STRUCTURAL

Fixations/5-19   C.I.A./5-34

In terms of ONE BRAIN, Structural category "outs" have to do with the effects of Dominant backbrain's most extreme stress response: total shut-down of the system. This results in a real sense of separation from the world, relationships, everything. The person feels unimportant, rigid and defeated.

FIXATIONS

When index-finger-to-thumb produces an indicator change, recheck Fixation. Should looking at black cause a second indicator change, **shine a beam of light on the glabella for 30 seconds to 1 minute** RETEST to verify correction.

If the correction comes up <u>more than once</u> at different stages of Age Recession, **as you shine the light turn the beam off and on in rapid repetitions.**

C.I.A.

In our western culture, most people exercise to strengthen their back muscles, unaware that the real issue is

BALANCE between back and <u>abdominal</u> muscles. A lack of balance between these two systems often results in low back pain. Yet most of us believe the answer to low back pain is MORE exercise for the back! Such exercise results in a continued cycle of painful episodes all based on an overly <u>rigid</u> set of spinal muscles.

In fact, the energy flows throughout the body can be blocked when a set of muscles "locks." For example, soldiers standing at attention or parade rest tend to lock their shoulder muscles, which in turn locks the muscles of the back, which in turn locks the knees. In a relatively short period of time - 10 to 15 minutes is usual - they're very likely to pass out and keel over. Locked muscles in the back of the leg and knee have cut off circulation and other energy-flows to the brain.

In daily life, we're our own Drill Sergeants. We snap to attention the second a threat comes into view. We go <u>rigid</u> with fear, and the same muscular lock takes place. While we rarely find ourselves in a "fixed physical position" for 10 or 15 minutes, the effect is much the same. Truth to tell, we go rigid mentally as well as physically. This correction does wonders to release and restore the energy balance.

THE CIA CORRECTION comes in two parts - the first of which consists of:

THE LEG MUSCLE RELEASE: Lie flat on your back, legs flexed, heels on the ground, the chin pulled in toward the neck. Next, keep your spinal column as flat as possible while you raise one leg as high as possible and make a mental note of the distance. Now vigorously <u>pluck</u> the

Achilles tendon behind your ankle. Next provide the same service for the Hamstring muscles in back of the knee and a few inches toward the buttocks. (Another image for the plucking action: it's like strumming a bass fiddle.)

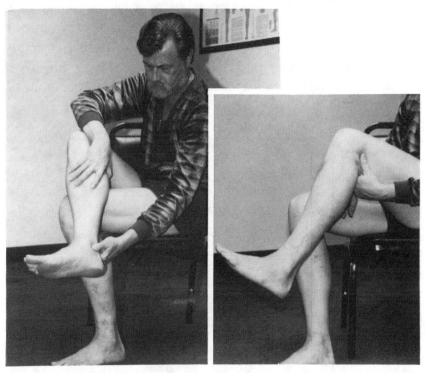

Once more raise the same leg as high as possible - can it go higher than before? Repeat the plucking/strumming on Achilles tendon and Hamstring. For a third time raise the leg as high as possible. Be aware if you can go higher with more comfort. Repeat the strum/plucking for a final time, relax and let your leg down to the ground. Now compare the way in which the two legs rest on the ground. Compare the way the two sides of your body feel in relation to the floor.

Repeat the correction with the other leg.

THE SHOULDER/NECK MUSCLE RELEASE: To relax tension in the shoulders, sit on a chair, your two feet flat on the floor. Place your right hand on your left shoulder in the middle of the trapezius muscle - midway between neck and shoulder. Apply enough pressure to stabilize the trapezius, meaning: "Hold it down firmly." Let the arm hang free. Now, <u>shrug</u> the left shoulder a couple of times. Next, <u>turn</u> the shoulder from front to back. Make perfect circles with the round tip of the shoulder, all the time firmly holding the trapezius so that it will play as slight a role as possible in the movement.

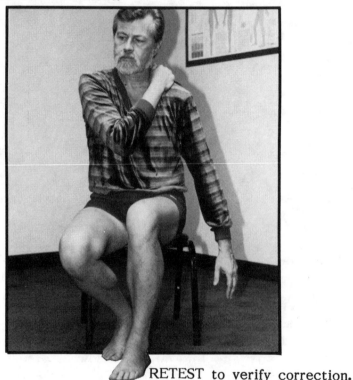

RETEST to verify correction.

REACTIVES

As mentioned before, the whole body reacts to trauma that we "see coming at us" and/or "hear as a threat." The muscles which were "on" at that moment suffer the emotional trauma the brain does and that trauma "freezes" them, forcing other muscles to take over to compensate for their less effective function. Correcting Short-Circuit: Eyes/Ears takes care of the eyes/ears only. These Reactive Corrections defuse the muscular freeze-patterns related to the body traumas produced by what we saw or heard.

When holding one hand over the person's mid-line crown-of-the-head while testing, an indicator change means it's time to correct a reactive condition. Such conditions are experienced primarily as chronic, inexplicable "return of pain" or "stiffness and soreness" apparently unrelated to current activities. (Of course, the truth is, they ARE related to right-now key-ins to past traumas we didn't defuse at the time!)

SHORT CIRCUIT: EYES
Make sure SHORT-CIRCUITED EYES have been corrected. Now have the person put the eyes in one position (such as up left) and hold them there while you check all five indicator muscles. If any of these muscles produce an indicator change, you have a reactive response.

The correction is the same as for SHORT-CIRCUITED EYES. Having alerted the neurons of the muscles involved, the correction defuses their reactive pattern. RETEST to verify correction.

SHORT CIRCUIT: EARS

Make sure SHORT-CIRCUITED EARS have been corrected. Now have the person turn the head in one direction and keep it turned that way while you check all five indicator muscles. If any of these muscles produce an indicator change, you have a reactive response.

The correction is the same as for SHORT CIRCUITED EARS. RETEST to verify correction.

CROSS-PATTERNING REACTIVES

Short-Circuited eyes happen because Dominant/CIA chose to "go blind" rather than confront a threat in the moment. Cross-Patterning Reactives trace back to a time when Dominant/CIA shut the door on Alternate's image-messages during a stressful period. No wonder the basics of correction show such similarity for these two reactive conditions.

Have your testee lie prone, eyes closed, and think of an X while you test all five indicator muscles. If any muscles show an indicator change, have the person maintain the mental image of X while doing the Cross-Patterning correction <u>lying down</u>. Now switch to the image of parallel lines and REPEAT. Alternate this cycle at least twice more. End with the person visualizing the X. RETEST (while visualizing the X) to verify correction. All muscles should stay strong. RETEST again, visualizing parallel lines. All muscles should test weak. Correction verified!

THE ONE BRAIN CORRECTION PROCEDURE

Now you're ready to begin the actual USE of the information presented thus far. Actually, you may have felt somewhat overwhelmed by the AMOUNT of information we've presented, and wondered how it would all come together. Well, this is how:

Having completed the examination, anchor "PRESENT TIME, RIGHT NOW" by testing.

Anchor the Emotional Stress Statement issue by testing - and remind your testee of that issue's **% of Negative Emotional Charge.**

Clear all Digitals in Present Time.

AGE RECESS until the indicator changes on a specific age. Find % of Negative Emotional Charge. Do Digitals and correct any "outs" until all hold strong and you have **0% of Negative Emotional Charge.**

Return to PRESENT TIME, RIGHT NOW. Do Digitals and correct any outs until all hold strong.

AGE RECESS again until the indicator changes. Find % of Negative Emotional Charge. Do Digitals and correct until all hold strong and you have **0% of Negative Emotional Charge.**

Return to **PRESENT TIME, RIGHT NOW.** Do Digitals and correct until all hold strong.

Continue to AGE RECESS until the indicator holds strong "from Present Time to conception." Return to PRESENT TIME, RIGHT NOW and check the Digitals, correcting until all hold strong.

Verify 0% of Negative Emotional Charge on the issue, and you've completed the Correction Procedure.

NOW RECHECK THE EXAMINATION

Test each and every category that caused an indicator change. Your testee will be amazed to discover that the indicator now holds strong on almost every category. (The word "almost" applies to very FEW people; usually ALL categories will have corrected.)

When an examination category still needs more work, respect how important that element is to understanding the nature of the individual's dyslexic pattern. Take a deep breath, roll up your mental sleeves and realize you've now reached the heart of the problem.

Follow the procedure outlined above to correct any remaining "outs" Begin by testing for % of Negative Emotional Charge on that specific issue.

STRESS THE IMPORTANCE OF THE HOMEWORK

Before the session ends, test the Digitals for the correction of choice to use as reinforcement "homework." Also test for how long "the body says" to do that homework.

Simply do the Digitals; when the indicator changes, test that Digital's categories. The next indicator change tells you the correction mode for homework. For the length of time: test "longer than 1 week, less than 1 week," etc. Then "how many times a day." And "how many repetitions each time." Trust the body to know what the mind can only guess.

Besides helping to reinforce the defusion, "homework" puts the responsibility for "getting better" square on the shoulders of the only person who can make the change - your testee. Repetition of the appropriate correction exercise, not only grooves in the neurological connection, it adds to self-esteem and self-image.

DEFUSE ANY % OF NEGATIVE EMOTIONAL CHARGE ON THE SESSION ITSELF

Because of the issues involved, the session itself may produce a % of Negative Emotional Charge. Stirring up painful memories, unblocking energy, and defusing embedded survival attitudes can create "unfulfilled feelings." Defusing such feelings assists your testee to leave the session with a sense of completeness.

Test for any % of Negative Emotional Charge on the session itself, then defuse whatever percentage remains via Digital Determination.

APPRECIATE WHAT YOU'VE ACCOMPLISHED

Realize the significance of what you and your testee have just done! You've identified the specifics of how that person blocked perception in a given area of learning and - having identified these energy blockages - you've defused them. What's more, your testee knows you've made a positive change because "what tested weak now holds strong."

In addition, Age Recession demonstrates that each of us chooses to create and maintain "learning dysfunctions" for reasons of survival "back then." Having defused that negative choice in the past, we free ourselves to make new and more profitable choices in the present - just as doing "homework" reinforces a more effective future.

EXAMINATION AND CORRECTION/A RUN-THROUGH

CAST OF CHARACTERS:
YOU (THE TESTOR) . . and . . LOIS (YOUR TESTEE)

PART I - THE EXAMINATION

YOU - How old are you, Lois? And, is there anything I need to watch for in muscle testing you - any sore shoulders, trick knees, a sore muscle - that sort of thing?

LOIS - I'm 14. And I'm just fine, no aches or pains.

YOU - All right, Lois. First thing, I'm going to take a look at your eyes to see if there's any observable sign of stress. Hmmm, there's more white showing under one iris than the other - we call that Second Stage Stress. It makes for depth perception problems. Have you noticed you've been have more accidents lately? (Circle YES and Lvl #2 on exam form.)

LOIS - Now that you mention it, I guess I have, sort of.

YOU - And next we want to **find a Clear Circuit Muscle** to use in testing. So I'm going to check out five of the easiest muscles to test - and I'll check all five in contraction and extension and make sure they're clear by using a spindle cell procedure that weakens, then strengthens them again. (Having done so, you select Anterior Deltoid as the indicator muscle, and make the appropriate exam notations.)

Good. Now we'll **check for SWITCHING** - which is another way of saying we're going to find out if both brain hemispheres are working together right now. So, first I'll

Basic One Brain   **CHAPTER 9-1**

test Anterior Deltoid on the right with one hand, which is to say "with one polarity." Then I change hands - meaning, I change polarity - and test again. Now, I'll test both arms at the same time, which is one polarity. Now I'll change hands - polarities - and test again. (Indicator change!)

LOIS - What does that mean?

YOU - It means that one hemisphere is over-riding the other. We correct switching before going on. I'll show you how to do that, and while you're making the correction, breathe! (Demonstrate all the correction points, holding the navel and rubbing K-27, etc.) Now make the correction on yourself. Good! Let's retest to be sure you're unswitched. (Now the indicator holds strong. Mark the exam.) Do you feel different at all?

LOIS - I think my head feels a little clearer. Maybe that was the breathing though. I guess I forget to breathe a lot.

YOU - Everybody forgets to breathe under stress. It's a good thing to remember. In fact, I'll be reminding you to BREATHE again and again. Breathing helps to center and balance, not to mention relax. So breathe!

OK, next we're going to **check out your Central and Governing Meridians** to see if they're flowing normally. I run my hand up the central meridian, and TEST. No indicator change. Now I run that meridian in reverse, from the lower lip down, and TEST. This time, the indicator changes. Good. (Mark OK on the exam.) Now we'll check out the governing meridian, so I do a hand-scan from tail bone to upper lip, and there's no indicator change. Next, we run it backward from upper lip to tail bone, TEST, and now we have an indicator change. (Mark the exam OK.) Before moving on, it's a good idea to run both those meridians back up in the right direction to strengthen them. (Do that now.)

LOIS - So what's next?

YOU - How you feel when you have to meet somebody else's **Set Standards** - how much Negative Emotional Charge comes on-line then. We'll check it by percentage on a scale of 1 to 100. Lois, which of your school subjects could stand the most improvement?

LOIS - Spelling. I hate spelling.

YOU - Think of taking a spelling test! (The indicator changes.) Let's see how much taking a spelling test stresses your body. I'm going to count up from zero to 100 in 10s, testing each time. 0 to 10 and TEST. 10 to 20 and TEST. 20 to 30 and TEST. 40 to 50 and TEST. (The indicator changes.) All right, so it's somewhere between 40 and 50. Let's find the exact number. I'll start with the highest number and test backward, the same as before. 50, and TEST. 49, and TEST. 48, and TEST. (Indicator holds strong!) OK, there's 48% negative charge on meeting standards set by others. Just a second while I mark that down on the exam . . .

> NOTE: If Lois's indicator didn't change while she thought about taking a spelling test, check for Blocking and/or check the indicator in extension on both sides.

YOU - Good. Now we'll find out how much Negative Emotional Charge comes on-line when you set the rules for somebody else.

LOIS - I never get to set the rules.

YOU - How about when you baby-sit? (Or whatever serves to identify the issue. Test for the % of Negative Emotional Charge and mark it on the exam.) Good. And now - what about when you set the standards for yourself? Lois, what's something you really want to be the best at in school?

LOIS - Swimming; I just love that.

YOU - So let's find out - when you compete at swimming - if you have any Negative Emotional Charge. (Do so, and fill in the blank on the exam). Good. OK, next come the **Reading Perception Tests.** And the first is <u>reading aloud.</u>

LOIS - Oh no, I hate to read aloud! I'm so embarrassed!

YOU - Just about everyone feels that way. Read aloud and other people make judgments about your reading.

LOIS - Yeah, like "that girl can't read"!

YOU - Well, the only real reason to do this part of the test is so that you'll appreciate how much better you read - and how much easier it is for you to read - aloud when we make the corrections. You'll hear and see that improvement before this session is over.

LOIS - You're kidding! Really?

YOU - Guaranteed. Are you ready? Just take this book and hold it with that hand while you read and I test your other arm while you're reading. I'll be doing a constant test for this one, too - that means if the indicator changes, I'll reposition it and continue testing. (Lois reads aloud, the indicator changes - and changes and changes.)

> NOTE: if there's no indicator change on the dominant arm in contraction, position it in extension and repeat the test, and/or repeat with the alternate arm in contraction and extension. If there's still no change, check for Blocking. Keep this in mind for all Reading Perception Tests. As a matter of fact, Blocking can show up as often as Switching, so if the indicator holds strong for inappropriate "answers," check for Blocking first and foremost. And as you proceed, continue to make the appropriate notations on the exam form, of course.

LOIS - That wasn't very good, was it?

YOU - You did fine. Now, can you tell me what you just read?

LOIS - Sure . . . uh. Something about . . . uh. I guess I don't remember. It's embarrassing.

YOU - Well, the next test won't be. This time, I'd like you to pick another paragraph and read backward. Start with the last word of the paragraph and read backward aloud.

LOIS reads backwards, with no indicator change - Why didn't the indicator change on that one?

YOU - Probably because nobody ever asked you to read backwards before. People don't read backwards, after all. You can't be judged on your performance, so - no stress. You're also reading word by word without having to make sense of what you're reading. Now would you please read silently, while I test your arm?

LOIS - Sure . . . (She reads silently as you test. The indicator changes, but not as dramatically as previously.) I think that was better than reading aloud.

YOU - Yes, it didn't stress you to the same degree. Can you tell me what you just read?

LOIS - Something about dyslexic children who got a grant program to work on that problem. Somewhere up north.

YOU - Good. Now, the next test is really fun. I'd like you to **say the alphabet, letter by letter,** while I test. Go slow, say one letter, pause while I test. Then another, and I'll test. Start with A and go right through to Z.

LOIS checks out "weak" on I, U, W, Y and Z. Make appropriate notations on the exam.

YOU - All right, now what I'd like you to do is **count from 0 through 10,** just as you did with the alphabet. Say a number, pause while I test, and so on. OK?

LOIS - Sure, why not? This is interesting. (Turns out the indicator changes on 1, 3, and 7. Mark the exam.) I wonder why those numbers came up?

YOU - Well, I imagine you're the only one who'd know. You're the authority, Lois - it's your arm.

LOIS - So what's next?

YOU - We call this test **Crossing the Mid-line.** Please write a sentence or two on the flip chart and sign your name.

LOIS - What should I write? Anything?

YOU - Sure, just a couple of sentences. And when you sign, use your legal signature - first name, middle initial and last name. Thank you. Good. Now that you've finished, I'd like you to look at your writing AS writing, while I TEST. Good. Now, look at just the left side of the writing, while I TEST. Good. Now, look at the middle portion only, while I TEST. Good. Now, look at the right side only, while I TEST. Now, let's see how you feel about your name. To begin with, look at your first name only, while I TEST. Next, look at your middle initial, while I TEST. And to finish, look at your last name. Good; thank you. (Mark the exam as appropriate.)

LOIS - Does everybody have as many muscle changes? I didn't think I was this dyslexic.

YOU - Lois, we're all dyslexic in one way or another. It may not turn up as a reading or writing problem, in fact most often it turns up as not getting along well with other people, or having a feeling that "I'm not OK." That's the same kind of dyslexic blind spot as a "comprehension problem" - it's just comprehension of another kind. And all of it is based on emotional stress. Once the stress goes, so does the problem. All right, are you ready for the next test?

LOIS - Sure. What do you want me to do?

YOU - The next series checks out any possible **Short-Circuits that involve the eyes.** So, with your eyes open - but keep your head straight ahead and still - I'd like you to look at the light (you're holding a penlight). I'll hold it in one position, and TEST. Then I'll move it to another position, and TEST again. First, look UP at the light. Good;

now to the RIGHT. Good; now over to the LEFT side. Good; now straight ahead. Thank you; now straight down. (Mark the exam as appropriate.)

Now, let's see if there's any difference when you close your eyes and change eye positions. Please close your eyes. Good. Now I'll say the direction to look, you put your eyes in that position and I'll TEST each in turn. Up . . to the right side . . to the left side . . straight ahead . . straight down. Good. (Mark the exam as appropriate.)

Next, we'll check **near and far eye positions** to see if any are stressors. I'll hold the light, you focus on that while I TEST. First, near. Next, at arm's length. Good; now the far distance, all the way to the corner over there. (Mark the exam with the results.)

This last eye test consists of your watching the light move back and forth twenty times. Keep your head still, just let your eyes move. By the way, this is the equivalent of actually reading for half an hour. The test indicates how much of a stressor that is to your system.

LOIS - I can tell you that right now!

YOU - Let's see what the body has to say. Here we go with the **eyes moving back and forth 20 times.** I'll count the number of repetitions. One, two, three, four . . (etc.).

LOIS - There, the indicator changed at twelve - I didn't think it would hold that long!

YOU - Some people can't hold their arms up after just three repetitions. (Mark exam as appropriate.) Ready for the next test category?

LOIS - I don't know. My arm's getting pretty tired.

YOU - We're just about done. Try taking a deep breath just before I test, then exhaling. Breathing makes a big difference; it helps the body to relax.

LOIS - Oh, that's right. I forgot. OK, I'm ready.

YOU - Next up is **Short-Circuit: Ears.** You turn your head to the right, and I'll TEST. Good; now turn your head to the left and I'll TEST again. (Mark the exam as to results.)

LOIS - On the Examination Sheet, the next category is **Fixation.** What does that mean?

YOU - It means that stress in the brain makes for a rigid spinal column for one thing. Let's find out whether that's the case with you. Just take a look at this piece of black paper while I TEST. (The indicator does NOT change. Mark "OK" on exam.)

LOIS - Well, I guess I'm not in fixation, since the muscle held strong.

YOU - Right. Keep that in mind, Lois. You're fine on Fixation right now in present time. It may be different when we do Age Recession, though. That's what's so interesting about the whole process. OK, now this next test, **Cross-Patterning,** is just as important. I'd like you to march in place - opposite arm and leg in motion, with your hands moving across the mid-line.

LOIS - How long do I march like that?

YOU - About half a dozen repetitions. Then, I'll TEST. Good. (This results in an indicator change. Mark the exam.) Now, I'd like you to march in place again, but this time use same arm/same leg and don't cross the mid-line. Then, I'll TEST again. (The ipsilateral test holds strong. Mark the exam.)

There's a second part to this test. It's to verify the first part which we just did. I'm going to draw a big X on the flip chart. Please look at the X, while I TEST. (Indicator changes.) Good. Now, I'm going to draw two parallel vertical lines. Please look at the II, while I TEST. (Indicator holds strong. Mark exam.)

LOIS - Is that the way it's supposed to be?

YOU - No, but we'll correct that before you leave today. This next test involves the **Hyoid** - that's a bone right under the jaw and over the Adam's apple. I'd like you to gently place your thumb and fingers on either side, above the Adam's apple and gently wiggle that area while I TEST. Good. Thank you. (Mark exam as appropriate to test results.)

The "Transverse Flow" is really the **Symbol of Infinity,** an 8 on its side. This test has to do with what happens when your energy field is disturbed from the outside. I'm going to make a waving motion up the mid-line of your body, then TEST. Good. (Mark result on the exam.) That's fine. Well, it looks like we only have three more exam categories left.

LOIS - Oh, good. My arm's still tired.

YOU - It's about <u>breathing,</u> remember? So, here we go with the **Nutrition/Genetic** test. I'm going to touch your glabella with my fingertips, and TEST.

LOIS - What's the glabella?

YOU - It's right here between the eyebrows where the two halves of the skull's frontal bones come together. And the pituitary is right behind it. OK, I touch two fingertips to the glabella and TEST.

LOIS - Well, the indicator stayed strong this time.

YOU - Yes, that category's in good shape. (Mark exam.)

LOIS - Looking ahead, what's CIA? Not the government agency, I hope!

YOU - Well, in a way it's your own unique Central Intelligence Agency. The first letters are the same, and in your Dominant brain hemisphere it serves much the same purpose. **CIA stands for the Common Integrative Area** which makes most of your decisions about what's right for you based on past experience. It's located on the temporal lobe behind your ear. I'm going to tap that area, continue to touch it, and TEST. Are you ready?

LOIS - Yes, and this time I'll remember to breathe, too.

YOU make the test, the indicator holds, you mark the exam - OK, there's just one category left. Lois, I'd like to pick some school subject you want to improve on.

LOIS - We already know that one. Spelling wins hands down. I'm so embarrassed about my spelling!

YOU - All right, let's make an **Emotional Stress Statement test** with spelling as the issue. I'd like you to say, "I want and trust my ability to spell well" while I test your arm in contraction. Then I want you to repeat that same statement while I test that same arm in extension. Ready?

LOIS - Sure. I want and trust my ability to spell well. (Contraction holds strong.) And here I go again: I want and trust my ability to spell well. (Extension changes the indicator.)

YOU - Now repeat that same statement while I test your other arm on the issue. (Lois does so, and the results are exactly opposite. Mark the exam accordingly.)

LOIS - That's amazing. I sure disagree with myself about wanting to spell well.

YOU - Now let's see what a negative statement on the issue brings to light. This time, say "I do NOT want or trust my ability to spell well," while I test one arm, first in contraction, then extension. Then we'll test the same statement with your other arm. (You do so and note the results on the exam.)

LOIS - What a double message!

YOU - It'll be a single positive message after we make the corrections. But first, let's find out the **% of Negative Emotional Charge** you have on the issue of spelling. (You do so, going up from 1 - 100 by increments of 10.)

LOIS - Golly, 93% of Negative Emotional Charge is a lot!

YOU - No wonder spelling's difficult, with all that negative over-energy attached to the issue!

PART II - THE CORRECTION PROCEDURE

REMEMBER THE MODEL:

1 - Find % of Negative Emotional Charge on the issue.
2 - Check and correct Digitals in Present Time.
3 - Age Recess. When the indicator changes, find % of Negative Emotional Charge, do Digitals until all hold strong and Negative Emotional Charge is 0.
4 - Return to Present Time - check and correct Digitals.
5 - Repeat Steps 3 and 4 until you have no indicator change from "Present Time to conception."
6 - Return to Present Time, check and correct Digitals, verify you have 0% Negative Emotional Charge on the issue.
7 - Defuse any % of Negative Emotional Charge on the session and you're done.

YOU - OK, Lois, here we go. First, I want to remind you that you had 93% Negative Emotional Charge on the issue of spelling, and that's what we're working on today - defusing that negative over-energy so you can lighten up on yourself and make progress with spelling. Before doing Age Recession to discover where you checked out on the issue, we need to make sure that your Energy Systems are clear in Present Time.

LOIS - Energy Systems? What's that mean?

YOU - (Briefly explain the Digital/Reactive Determinators.) So it's a matter of checking the basic categories of how we stress ourselves out. Now do you want to "do the fingers" - or would you rather I did?

LOIS - This first time, why don't you?

YOU - Fine. I'll say the name of the category, then TEST, so you'll know what category causes the indicator to change. That's what we're after: defusing the negative stress that makes the indicator change. You'll know that negative stress has been defused when the muscle holds strong after correction. OK?

LOIS - OK!

YOU - I'm going to be testing your arm several times in a row, now. I'll keep the pressure light. But if your arm gets tired, let me know and I'll change to the extended position or use another muscle.

LOIS - Yes, and I'll remember to take a deep breath and let it out slowly while you test.

YOU - I'll say the name of each Digital in turn and then test. Electrical, and TEST. Emotional, and TEST. Nutrition/Genetic, and TEST. Structural, and TEST. Reactives, and TEST. (No indicator changes.) Well, the Digitals are fine in present time. That mean's we're ready to do Age Recession.

LOIS - I'll bet you're glad I'm not 95 years old!

YOU - You're 14, right? OK, let's start with **Present time,** right now, to age 14, and TEST. No indicator change, so let's continue: 14 to 10, and TEST. We're clear there, so: 10 to birth, and TEST - and the indicator <u>changes.</u>

LOIS - Now what?

YOU - Now we find out exactly how old you were when "it" happened, whatever "it" may be. I'll be counting down from 10, and testing each age. When the indicator changes, that should be the one. 10, and no change. 9, and no change. 8, and no change. 7, and no change. 6, no change. 5, and we get a <u>change.</u> Let's verify that: 4, and the muscle holds strong. 6, and the muscle holds strong. 5, and we test and the indicator changes. 5, it is. And how much Negative Emotional Charge? (You test for the figure.) So, it's 84% at age 5.

All right, now I'm doing the Digitals again. I'll say the category name, and TEST. Electrical. Emotional. Nutrition/Genetic. Structural. There we go, the indicator changed on Structural. So we have two items to check under the Structural Determinator - Fixations and CIA.

LOIS - How do we check them?

YOU - The same way as during the Examination, starting with Fixation. Look at this piece of black paper, while I TEST. (The indicator changes.) Lois, remember when we tested Fixation during the Exam, your arm held strong? But now, back at age 5, looking at black makes the indicator change.

LOIS - How do you correct for Fixation?

YOU - I take my trusty penlight and shine its beam right between your eyebrows. You can close your eyes if you want to. (You make the correction.) Good. Now let's retest and see if that worked. Take another look at the piece of black paper while I test. (Lois looks, you test and the indicator holds strong.)

OK, it looks like we fixed Fixation at age 5. But now we need to be sure that was the only "out." Let's go through the Digitals again. I'll say the age and the category name while I touch that fingertip to my thumb, then test. Here we go: Age 5, holds strong. Electrical, holds strong. Emotional, holds strong. Nutrition/Genetic, holds strong. Structural, holds strong - which it didn't just now. And Reactives, holds strong. Good! Age 5 doesn't make the indicator change now, nor does Structural, nor any other category. Let's recheck % of Negative Emotional Charge. (You do so.) 0 - good! It's time to come back to the present.

Age 5 to 10, and TEST. Good: 10 to 14, and TEST. 14 to present time, right now, and TEST. Good. Now, we'll do the Digitals again in present time. Electrical, holds strong. Emotional, holds strong. Nutrition/Genetic, holds strong. Structural, holds strong - and Reactives, holds strong. We're just fine in present time.

LOIS - Now what?

YOU - We keep Age Recessing until we're clear at conception. OK, here we go. Present time, right now to age 14, and TEST. 14 to 10 and - we get an indicator change. All right, we start back with the highest number: 14, and TEST. 13, and TEST. 12, and TEST. 11, and - the indicator changes. Let's verify: age 10, and - the indicator changes again. 9, and - the indicator changes a third time in a row.

Well, Lois, the indicator should only change on <u>one age</u>, which means that most likely you've SWITCHED. Remember during the exam, I showed you how to unswitch - rubbing all the switch points? Take a deep breath and rub them all in turn. Then I'll check you out. (Lois does so, you do the Switching Test and discover that she's now unswitched, so it's time to proceed.)

YOU - OK, we'll take it back to pre-switching. Age 12, and TEST. 11, and TEST and the indicator changes. Let's verify. 10, and TEST. The indicator holds strong. 11, and the indicator changes again, so we're fine. Percentage of Negative Emotional Charge? (You test for it.) More than 50? 60? 70? 80? Indicator change. So - 79? 78? 77 - and it holds strong at 77%. 77% at age 11. Now I'll do the Digitals and test after each one: Electrical. Emotional. Nutrition/Genetic. Structural - and the indicator changes. Lois, stressors often come in patterns, so chances are good Fixation is out again. Look at black while I test, and the indicator <u>changes.</u> We'll correct Fixation the same way as before - shining a beam of light between the eyebrows. Good. Now look at black again and I'll test. Good, it's holding strong, so let's test for % of charge. Zero? Good, it's zero. Next, I retest the Structural Determinator - and now that holds strong, too. Next we retest the age that caused the indicator change - 11 - and that holds strong, so we can now come back to Present Time.

LOIS - And we do the Digitals again, to see if I'm clear on them in Present Time, right?

YOU - Right, so: Electrical. Emotional. Nutrition/Genetic. Structural. And Reactives. They all hold strong.

LOIS - So it's Age Recession time again.

YOU - Age 14 to 10, and TEST. 10 to birth, and the indicator changes. Good: 10, and TEST. 9, and TEST. 8, and TEST. 7, and the indicator changes. Good, let's verify: 6, and hold strong. 7 it is. Percentage of Negative Emotional Charge? (You test and discover it's 96% at age 7.) Good, and now I'll test each of the Digitals in turn. (You do so.) Electrical is the only one that makes the indicator change.

LOIS - Now we run through the Electrical category and find which one's out - and with 96% Negative Charge on it, too. Wow, that's a lot!

YOU - Yes, it is. So let's check Electrical. First I'll test for Transverse Flow, making a wave-motion across the torso, and TEST. No change. OK, Lois, gently wiggle the Hyoid and I'll TEST. No change. All right, look at the "X" I drew on the flip chart, and the indicator changes. Now look at the parallel lines, and the muscle holds strong. Which means we need to do the Cross-Patterning correction.

LOIS - Which is?

YOU - You march in place with opposite arm and leg. Swing your hand across the mid-line and touch the opposite knee. Good, keep going. Now when I say "change," switch to same side marching - touch the right knee with the right hand, left knee, left hand. Change! Good, keep it up. Next, when I say "change," go back to opposite hand and knee. Change! Good, touch your left knee with your right hand, swing right across the mid-line. Good, left hand/right knee, right hand/left knee. Good. Now keep marching and move your eyes all "around the clock" and straight ahead - clockwise first, then counter-clockwise. Good.

LOIS - How much longer?

YOU - That's fine. You can stop now, and look at the X. And the indicator holds strong, which is what it's supposed to. Now look at the parallel lines, and the indicator changes. Good! And % of Negative Emotional Charge at age 7? 0? Good!

LOIS - When we did the exam, wasn't I strong on parallel lines and weak on the "X"?

YOU - Right, which means this correction is "the big one." Now your Dominant Brain Hemisphere is allowing Alternate's input and not tuning it out. In fact this is such a breakthrough, I want to track back on Cross-Patterning as a single category from where we are at age 7. Keep the X in mind and let's see if we can find an earlier time when that was the basic issue.

Age 6, and TEST. Age 5, and TEST. 4, and TEST. 3, and the indicator changes. Good. Percentage of Negative Emotional Charge? Another big one - 93%. So now, look at the X, and the indicator changes. Look at the parallel lines, and the indicator holds strong. Now do the Cross-Patterning correction, just like you did at age 7. And keep moving your eyes around the clock and straight ahead, then counter-clockwise. Change to same side marching. Good, now change back to the cross-over pattern. Keep the eyes moving. OK! That's probably enough. Let's see if the correction worked for age 3. Look at the X, and the indicator <u>now holds strong</u>. Look at the parallel lines, and the indicator changes. Good, that's the way we want it. Let's check the % of Charge - still 96? No, says the indicator. Less than 10? Yes, says the indicator. Less than 5? Yes. 4? 3, and the indicator holds strong. So do another Cross-Patterning correction. (She does so). Good, let's check the charge. Zero? And now that holds strong. Is it anything other than zero? No, says the indicator. Good!

Let's continue tracking back. Age 2, and TEST. 1 to birth, and the indicator changes. OK, here we go again: Percentage of Negative Emotional Charge? (You test for it.) 83% at age 2. Now look at the X, and the indicator changes. Parallel lines, and it holds strong. Do the Cross-Patterning correction again. March in place, opposite arm and leg for several repetitions, then same side, then back to cross-over. And the eyes go around the clock and straight ahead as you march, then counter-clockwise. Very good; you really do that well! So, let's check the result. Now at Age 1, look at the X, and now that tests <u>strong,</u> and parallel lines makes the indicator change. And the % of Negative Emotional Charge? Good - it's down to 0. Fine; that's just what we want!

Is there an earlier time when Cross-Patterning was out? Age 1 to birth now holds strong. Birth to conception, holds strong. So let's come back to Present Time. Conception to birth, holds strong. Birth to 10, holds strong. 10 to present time, right now, holds strong. So now look at the X while I test, and the indicator holds strong. Look at parallel lines - and the indicator changes. Good! Defusing the past defused the present!

LOIS - That's amazing!

YOU - Yes, but we haven't checked out the Digitals to be sure present time is on the All Clear, too. So, let's run through them, while I test: Electrical, holds strong. Emotional, holds strong. Nutrition/Genetic, holds strong. Structural, holds strong. And Reactives - holds strong, too.

LOIS - Are we done?

YOU - Almost. Let's be sure. We know we're clear in Present Time. So, present time to 14 - holds strong. 14 to 10 - holds strong. 10 to birth - holds strong. Birth to conception - holds strong. So, back we come: conception to birth - holds strong. Birth to 10 - holds strong. 10 to present time, right now - holds strong. Let's check the Digitals now. Electrical - holds strong. Emotional - holds strong. Nutrition/Genetic - holds strong. Structural - holds strong. And Reactives - holds strong. Yes, that's it. When there's no indicator change on Age Recession and the Digitals, we've reached the end of the session.

LOIS - But what about all those indicator changes I had during the Examination?

YOU - Let's check them out. I think you'll be amazed at the results now. We'll take them one by one, right from the top.

(You do just that. Retest all "outs" in each exam category. Lois is surprised at first, then amazed. There's no indicator change on anything; everything holds strong - including both positive and negative Emotional Stress Statements - AND the % of Negative Emotional Charge on the issue of spelling is 0.)

LOIS - I'm really pleased. But how long will this "hold?"

YOU - Even if you did <u>nothing</u> more, you'd notice a general improvement in your reading, comprehension and writing, Lois. BUT - if you want to speed that up, and increase your effectiveness, there's **homework** that'll really help. Let's test for the best one by doing the Digitals. Electrical - and the indicator changes. So let's go down the list of Electrical's categories. Take a look at the X while I test - and the indicator changes. Is that the best one? Yes. Is there a better one? The indicator says "no." So it's Cross-Patterning. And how long to do it? Longer than one week? Yes. Longer than a month? No. Longer than three weeks? No. <u>Less</u> than three weeks? No. So it's three weeks. Yes. More than once a day? Yes. Twice a day. Yes. Morning and evening. Yes. Is it anything else? No.

LOIS - So I'm to do the cross-over marching and the eye movements morning and night - and maybe when I'm feeling stressed, too?

YOU - You bet! Do the exercises twice a day and whenever you feel it'd be a good idea until I see you next. How about a week from today, same time and station?

LOIS - OK by me. This stuff's fun!

YOU - All right, last of all we'll check to be sure you have no Negative Emotional Charge on the session itself. (You do so and find that Lois has 7% charge to release. Doing Digitals identifies the correction as Fixation under the Structural Determinator. You make the correction, then verify that Lois has 0% Negative Emotional Charge on the session itself. Session complete!)

TRANSVERSE FLOW	Waving motion across body	Hold navel and forehead
SIGNS OF STRESS	Observe eyes	Recheck after session
SWITCHING	Change hands on indicator muscle Left/Right	Left/Right - Navel + K-27 Up/Down - rub upper/lower lip while holding navel Front/Back - navel + coccyx
CENTRAL/GOVERNING	Trace with hand and test	Flush meridian
SET STANDARDS	% of Negative Emotional Charge	Recheck after defusion
READING PERCEPTION	Read: aloud and silently Check comprehension	K-27 with eye movement, alphabet or Cook's method
ALPHABET/NUMBERS	Say aloud and test	Trace in air, in hand and in imagination
CROSSING MID-LINE	Test written line in 3rds	Infinity symbol
SHORT-CIRCUIT EYES	Test with eyes open/closed in all five directions	Eye points
SHORT-CIRCUIT EARS	Turn head and test	Pull/extend ear
FIXATION	Look at black	Shine light on glabella
CROSS-PATTERNING	Look at X and II	Alternate cross-over exercise with ipsilateral
HYOID	Gently move Hyoid while testing	Identify muscle: pinch belly of muscle.
NUTRITION/GENETIC	Touch glabella with two fingers	RNA/DNA - water
CIA	Tap and hold behind dominant ear	Strum ankle tendons and hamstrings. Stabilize upper trapezius and rotate shoulder.
STRESS STATEMENT	"I want and trust . . ." "I do not want . . ."	Emotional Stress Defusion techniques and Body Scan

SUMMARY

ONE BRAIN CORRECTION SCHEMA

A | Clear Circuit Indicator | **Switching**

B | Digitals in Present Time

Correct any Indicator Changes

C | Age Recession | **% of Negative Emotional Charge** | **Digitals**

Correct any Indicator Changes

THUMB/LITTLE Electrical	THUMB/RING Emotional	THUMB/MIDDLE Nutritional	THUMB/INDEX Structural	1 1/2" ABOVE HEAD Reactive
Transverse flow	ESD	RNA/DNA	Fixations	Short-circuit: Eyes
Hyoid	Body scan	Water	C.I.A.	Short-circuit: Ears
Reading perception				Cross-patterning
Cross-patterning				
Short-circuit: Eyes				
Short-circuit: Ears				
Alphabet/Counting				
Crossing the Mid-line				

0% Negative Emotional Charge at age

D | Return to Present Time

Check and correct DIGITALS and continue AGE RECESSION until PRESENT TIME to CONCEPTION holds strong.

E | Verify 0% Negative Emotional Charge on Issue

F | 0% Emotional Charge on Session

ADDENDUM

THE BEHAVIORAL BAROMETER

CHOICE

CONSCIOUS

ACCEPTANCE

Choosing to • Approachable
Optimistic • Acceptable
Adaptable • Worthy
Deserving • Open

WILLING

Receptive • Adequate
Prepared • Answerable
Encouraging • Refreshed
Invigorated • Aware

INTEREST

Fascinated • Tuned-in
Needed • Welcomed
Understanding • Appreciated
Essential • Caring

ANTAGONISM

Attacked • Bothered
Questioned • Burdened
Annoyed • Indignant
Opposing • Inadequate

ANGER

Incensed • Furious
Over-wrought • Fuming
Seething • Fiery
Belligerent • Hysterical

RESENTMENT

Hurt • Embarrassed
Wounded • Used/abused/confused
Unappreciated • Rejected
Dumb • Offended

SUBCONSCIOUS

ENTHUSIASM

Amused • Jubilant
Admirable • Attractive
Delighted • Excited
Alive • Trusting

ASSURANCE

Motivated • Daring
Protected • Bold
Brave • Considered
Affectionate • Proud

EQUALITY

Lucky • Co-operative
Involved • Purposeful
Reliable • Concerned
Sincere • Productive

HOSTILITY

Trapped • Picked-on
Put-upon • Frustrated
Deprived • Sarcastic
Vindictive • With-holding

FEAR OF LOSS

Let-down • Not-heard
Bitter • Disappointed
Threatened • Over-looked
Frightened • Unwelcome

GRIEF AND GUILT

Betrayed • Conquered
Discouraged • Unacceptable
Self-punishing • Despondent
Defeated • Ruined

BODY

ATTUNEMENT

In tune with • Congruent
In balance • Creative
Perceptive • Appreciative
Tender • Gentle

ONENESS

Quiet • Safe
Calm • At peace
Unified • Completed
Fulfilled • At-one-ment

INDIFFERENCE

Pessimistic • Immobilized
Rigid • Numb
Stagnant • Unfeeling
Destructive • Disconnected

SEPARATION

Uncared for • Unloved
Unacceptable • Loveless/unlovable
Unimportant • Melancholy
Morbid • Deserted

CHOICE/NO CHOICE

THE BEHAVIORAL BAROMETER: WHAT IT IS/HOW IT WORKS

The Barometer maps a sure progression from present to past and past to future (in terms of) emotional states and desired states of mind. This progression begins with **CHOICE** - or <u>the lack of it</u>.

If we make a conscious, positive CHOICE in present time to take responsibility for handling our emotions, the progression toward DESIRED STATES OF MIND (the left side) starts with **ACCEPTANCE** of what IS <u>as is</u>. Now we're released from past expectations, past reactions and past patterns. What's more, we're ready to perceive new options. Plus: having made the CHOICE of ACCEPTANCE, we become **WILLING** to implement those new options. The result of WILLING is increased **INTEREST** - both in the developing situation and in OURSELVES.

All of which takes place on a **CONSCIOUS** level of awareness. We know exactly what we're doing and we feel good about it. Yet also on the CONSCIOUS LEVEL lives the progression toward the emotional pit (the left side) which results from the <u>lack of a positive CHOICE</u> to take responsibility. **ANTAGONISM** unleashes **ANGER**, then - when that fails to resolve the situation - **RESENTMENT**.

This progression now reaches the **SUBCONSCIOUS** where it keys-in and/or reinforces similar patterns from the past. If have a track-record of taking responsibility, we get the good of this reinforcement. We don't have to manufacture

ENTHUSIASM, it's just automatically ours. And as EN-THUSIASM persists, it evolves into an **ASSURANCE** that supports us as a given. We're not "thinking ASSURANCE," we ARE assured - which graduates us into the **EQUALITY** state of mind. There's an inner (subconscious) awareness that we're EQUAL to almost any situation, trial or relation-ship.

Alas, what if the progression into the SUBCONSCIOUS is based on the failure to CHOOSE responsibly? Instead of true ENTHUSIASM, we begin the **HOSTILITY** game - acting out positives to mask the negatives within. Since that never works, the pay off is **FEAR OF LOSS** which in turn tumbles us into **GRIEF AND GUILT**. Now there's nothing we're EQUAL to and nothing to be done except despair. The proof that we'll "always" botch it up is there; the reinforce-ment is complete. Our past patterns have soured present perception and guarantee similar reactions in the future.

These reactive patterns (positive and negative alike) are layered into our memory banks from conception onward. There was always a "right now/present time" in Conscious-ness. When the present became the past, the Subconscious stored its record of what has once been present time. As days and months and years rolled on, every intense experience remained "on file." And the MOST intense experiences - both negative AND positive - devolved into the very nature of our being, stored in every cell affected by that experience, muscle, organ and bone as well as brain.

We call this level of awareness **BODY**. **BODY** represents the deep unconscious, CELLULAR MEMORY. In this sense, it also represents the SPIRIT - that essence which maintains the unity of body/mind.

If the progression into BODY awareness has been positive, we experience a real **ATTUNEMENT** to our world, the people and events of which we are a part. Continued ATTUNEMENT leads to a sense of **ONENESS** (as Shakespeare said in quite another context, "'tis a consum-mation devoutly to be wished"!) on a universal level. Unfortunately, should the progression have been toward the pit, we're in it now - bleak **INDIFFERENCE** awaits and, finally, we come to **SEPARATION**.

Obviously, the CHOICE is ours. Not as obviously, **CHOICE** itself is the third and final factor on the BODY level of awareness. The reason? Because both ONENESS and SEPARATION are never ends in themselves. Completion is completion. Both begin a new cycle, positive or negative as the case may be depending on the nature of the **CHOICE** that starts this new cycle. Also the body makes most of our CHOICES for us. It would never trust our CONSCIOUS SELF to run the chemical plant to digest our food, or keep us breathing, or let us take charge of the nervous system or circulation, etc.

TWO SIDES TO THE COIN

Truth to tell, each negative emotional state is as valuable as each desired state of mind. For instance, when we're finally fed up with RESENTMENT, ANGER is one appropriate means of clearing the air. GRIEF is an invaluable acknowledgement of heart-felt loss, and GUILT can be a salutary motivation every now and then - just as INDIF-FERENCE to pain may be the only way to make it through the day. Certainly SEPARATION delayed creates more problems than delay can ever solve.

In fact, we're never "purely" one level or another. It's a matter of yin and yang - a matter of "more of one than the other," not an absence of one or the other. ACCEPTANCE of a situation "as is" doesn't free us completely from the ANTAGONISM which prompted that CHOICE. In the same sense, we choose SEPARATION because we want ONENESS with something other than we have. Think of each Barometric level as paired.

As an image, visualize the Barometer as consisting of eight golden coins, each representing more value as they go from

ACCEPTANCE/ANTAGONISM to ONENESS/SEPARA-TION. There is no single coin for **CHOICE** because **CHOICE is the gold of which all the coins are made.**

ACCEPTANCE is stamped on one side of the first coin, ANTAGONISM on the other. The second coin reads WILL-INGNESS on one side, the other side reads ANGER - and so it goes through ONENESS/SEPARATION. Again, the coins are gold and the gold is CHOICE. CHOICE is the true coin of the realm, no matter what's stamped on either face.

Such being the case, <u>when you identify a negative feeling, you also know exactly what you WANT</u>. Just as important, your DENIAL that you can have what you want is based on your denial that you have a **CHOICE** in the matter.

THE LITTLE WORDS
ARE BIG ONES

The Barometer's major categories speak to the three basic levels of awareness: Conscious, Subconscious and Body. Each paired step of that progression indicates a single <u>general</u> category. Under each of these general categories you'll see a list of "little words." These, too, have their progression leading from one category to the next in a step by step process.

<u>Read them across and down.</u>

For instance, under **ACCEPTANCE** they're as follows:

Choosing to/Approachable
Optimistic/Acceptable
Adaptable/Worthy
Deserving/Open

Here's the progression.

Once we've CHOSEN TO accept the situation as IS, we relax and become a whole lot more APPROACHABLE. That takes off a lot of pressure, and the others involved feel safe enough to approach us, try to work things out. That inspires a more OPTIMISTIC attitude on our part (and, hopefully, theirs). Such OPTIMISM makes the situation more ACCEPTABLE for all hands. And when we find ourselves ACCEPT-ABLE in a situation, our creative juices start to flow - making us feel much more WORTHY. After all, we've taken charge, taken responsibility for our own reactions, and Lord knows that's a positive plus! Feeling WORTHY evolves into a sense of DESERVING - deserving more of the best from ourselves because it feels so good. That frees us to be more OPEN - now we're **WILLING** to reach even further.

So it goes - onward to ONENESS or SEPARATION depending on the CHOICE (or denial of CHOICE) which began the cycle. And the reverse is true, too. It's a fascinating way to chart your course toward ONENESS or toward SEPARA-TION.

AND RE. DESIRED STATE OF MIND/NEGATIVE EMOTION: always check to discover WHICH SIDE OF THE BAROMETER you're working with in a given session. Find out upfront, and underscore that DESIRED STATE OF MIND = what the person WANTS MORE OF. This doesn't mean he or she has attained that positive state, but the desire is there. With this in mind, check the other side of the Barometric coin and its paired little word for the rest of the story.

For instance, DESIRED STATE OF MIND SIDE is indicated and ASSURANCE/Motivated shows up. Chances are, the person WANTS TO FEEL ASSURANCE, WANTS TO FEEL MOTIVATION, but "the truth" might read, "It's difficult to be motivated and assured when you're feeling let-down and unsure of yourself." Agreement on that score provides the opportunity to brainstorm options which build toward having the longed-for ASSURANCE/Motivation.

THAT'S RIGHT:
THE LITTLE WORDS ARE COINS, TOO

Just as with the Barometer's major categories, the little words have their opposite numbers. They work together on the yin/yang principle. When you identify which little word applies, take a look at the little word in exactly the same position on the "other side of the coin." This gives you a more complete picture of what's going on.

For instance, let's say you're "out" on **ANGER.**

Having identified the general category, test to find which little word applies as well. If it turns out to be OVER-WROUGHT and you wonder why, just take a look at the little word in exactly the same position under **WILLING.** It's PREPARED. Chances are, you're OVER-WROUGHT because you're not PREPARED to handle that confrontation, make that report, or accept responsibility for your part of the immediate angrifying situation. With that in mind, you might be more WILLING to make the kind of positive **CHOICE** that will bring more of what you truly desire and less of the mess you have on your hands right now.

Remember: the little words are a work in <u>progress</u> LEFT SIDE or RIGHT. They map your way in both directions, providing milestones along the path - not to mention food for thought!

NOTE: There are no further descriptive words for **CHOICE.** When CHOICE comes up on the BODY level, it means just that: a CHOICE needs to be made right now to release the BODY level stressors - or a past CHOICE/vow/decree needs to be defused through Age Recession.

WHEN TO USE THE BAROMETER

At Three In One Concepts, we use the Barometer to further identify and clear <u>every indicated "out,"</u> be it a so-called physical imbalance or emotional stressor. There's no separating physical and emotional. Every physical pain has an emotional concomitant. In a given moment, one may predominate but both are present. To defuse one without defusing the other is like handing your client half a hundred dollar bill.

It's the same hassle as being content to defuse a dyslexic in present time without using Age Recession to alleviate the CAUSOR of that dyslexia. Sure, defusing present time can provide remarkable and immediate results. But how long does that defusion "hold"? Only until the next stressor overwhelms the person. Then it's back to zero - and fast! Even daily exercises that help dyslexic corrections hold in present time aren't proof against renewed emotional trauma. That's why we always use Age Recession with our private clients. Combined with the Barometer, it's simply invaluable - and soooooooooooooooooo specific.

FOR YOURSELF, use the Barometer to identify what you're really feeling and wanting in any troublesome situation. Use it as an aid in decision-making - to clarify your thinking - to understand your emotional options at any given point in time.

Knowing that the little word PROUD (under **ASSURANCE**) lives opposite UNWELCOME (under **FEAR OF LOSS**), at Three In One we're never too proud to find out WHY we've checked out of responsibility - however unwelcome that identification might feel at first and especially if it flies in the face of some cherished expectation. But that's only momentary. In fact, it becomes a JOY to discover the what/where/how of our check-outs. Once we know the problem, we're halfway to the solution, after all. The whole idea of self-health maintenance is to get better. It seems a terrible waste of time to help others and not get the good of it for ourselves.

WHEN WORKING WITH OTHERS, we suggest you use the Barometer (and Age Recession if you're comfortable with it) to further identify the stressors relating to any physical imbalance. It will enrich your work remarkably, plus giving your client further "proof" that a positive change has taken place. A person's whose indicator muscle changed on **GRIEF AND GUILT** with CONQUERED as its little word will be enormously relieved when the muscle "holds strong" after Frontal/Occipital Holding. (See Basic ONE BRAIN or UNDER THE CODE).

Plus, during F/O HOLDING, you can now use your verbal skills to draw the person's consciousness toward the desired state of mind: **EQUALITY/COOPERATIVE.** Using the other side of the Barometric coin and its appropriate little word opens up new vistas of educated-guess listening/ feedback ability!

THE PROCESS

Our experience tells us to take certain steps BEFORE testing for any specifics your testee might believe is a problem. We use the following pattern to guarantee the highest grade of feedback possible from the body in question.

PRIOR TO ALL ELSE IN YOUR TESTING PROCEDURE:

BE SURE YOU HAVE A CLEAR MUSCLE CIRCUIT FOR TESTING PURPOSES

CHECK FOR POSSIBLE OVERLOAD

We believe this two-step ritual is absolutely imperative before muscle-testing anyone for anything. It's a matter of insurance. Were a muscle to be BLOCKED through stress, we wouldn't know unless we checked for Clear Muscle Circuit. A blocked test muscle holds strong PERIOD, registering a positive response to everything. No valid feedback is possible from the body.

The reverse holds true should your testee be "OVERLOAD." A Dominant Brain (right side of Barometer) over-ride invalidates Alternate Brain's input (left side of the Barometer). The result shows up as inaccurate feedback which makes muscle-testing a waste of time and energy. (If these steps (and/or Frontal/Occipital Holding) sound unfamiliar to you, read our workshop texts for **ONE BRAIN** and/or **UNDER THE CODE**.)

Having made sure we have an unblocked body/brain, our job now is to make sure the testee has no emotional lock-ons that might impede clarity of feedback. This means testing the three levels of awareness in turn. When all three levels hold strong, we have the testee's full <u>right now</u> attention, so:

SAY: "PRESENT TIME, RIGHT NOW" AND TEST

If the indicator muscle changes, use F/O Holding AND CONTROLLED BREATHING until the muscle tests strong. When it does:

SAY: "CONSCIOUS" AND TEST

This is a blanket test for <u>all three Barometric coins</u> on the CONSCIOUS LEVEL OF AWARENESS. If there's an indicator change, make note of it, then move right along.

SAY: "SUBCONSCIOUS" AND TEST

Again, this is a blanket test of the three Barometric coins on the Subconscious level of awareness. Make note of any change in the indicator muscle and proceed:

SAY: "BODY" AND TEST

Ditto the above. Remember that **CHOICE** is the third category to test for at this level of awareness.

IF THE INDICATOR MUSCLE CHANGED ON ANY LEVEL:

FIRST: Determine whether the testee is LEFT SIDE - or RIGHT SIDE on the Barometer.

SECOND: Test to identify which of the three Barometric words causes an indicator change on that level.

THIRD: Test to find the appropriate little word involved (and check out its Barometric opposite for additional insight).

USE F/O HOLDING and your listening skills for defusion. Retest. You want a strong indicator response on all three levels before proceeding.

To us, the above procedure is invaluable. Sometimes, just taking these few simple steps defuses "the problem that walked in the door." Whether it does or not, the process prepares and calms the testee for whatever work follows. (Please note that "prepares" and "calms" are forms of two key little words: **WILLING/Prepared** - versus ANGER/Overwrought - and **ONENESS/Calm** - versus SEPARATION/ Unacceptable.)

ABOUT THE BAROMETER
ABOUT THREE IN ONE CONCEPTS

Throughout the ages, humankind has understood the levels of awareness. The Egyptians had many different hieroglyphics for the word we translate incorrectly/inadequately as "soul" or "spirit." Each of these different pictographs defines a distinctly different function of awareness within the body/mind/spirit. In effect, the Hindu Vedas provide the same kind of overview (represented in spades by what evolved as the caste system, a personification of this concept). The Sufis, too, developed the concept. L. Ron Hubbard had his version - the Tone Scale. But the Behavioral Barometer is strictly our development.

It's interesting to us, the symbology involved. There are eight major categories/coins with **CHOICE** intrinsic to each. And it turned out there are eight little words for each of the eight major categories. All of which defined itself through Clear Circuit Muscle Testing at this address.

That's right, we test EVERYTHING, every concept, every new technique, every new usage - even the names and dates of our workshops. If "it" isn't right for us at Three In One, we discard it or put it on the back burner until further insight makes it work for us. And if that seems a shade weird to you, understand that we've found we can trust Clear Muscle Circuit testing - we trust it implicitly, to the point there's never a wasted discussion, nor do we allow idle speculation to waste time. Intellectual justification? Why bother when we can learn "the truth" immediately by testing?

We understand that such truth is strictly our truth, though. Whatever programs, concepts or skills we represent are just that: our truth. It works for us. So with that in mind, we anticipate you'll accept our version of truth for what it inspires within you. Working with the Barometer, you'll gain your own insights, devise your own way of making it work best for you. Enjoy the depth of understanding it releases in yourself and those with whom you share its power.

DEFUSION SHEETS

The following Defusion sheets for Basic ONE BRAIN were put together by Facilitator Sharon Promislow from Canada. She has her own center called ENHANCED LEARNING & INTEGRATION, INC., 3584 Rockview Place, West Vancouver, B.C. Canada V7V 3H3 (604) 922-8811.

If you use the balances in order - 1 to 5 - you'll gain the confidence of doing the work. Her format layers the new learning in digestible chunks, all within the context of actual balances with a successful outcome.

We assume you have worked through the preliminary learning processes of *Tools Of The Trade* Balances 1, 2, and 3. *Basic ONE BRAIN* I serves as the review of all the basic skills learned in *Tools Of The Trade.*

Balances 2, 3 and 4 are the pre-tests and corrections in segments, all the time building up experience with digital determination and successful balancing.

We thank Sharon for her dedication and creativity.

BASIC ONE BRAIN - Balance 1

SET-UP MUSCLES - test contraction and extension

Chap. 3-16	Clear Circuit muscles	(correct blocking)
Chap. 4-3	Overload	(Rub K-27's and hold navel)
Chap. 4-7	Central Meridian	(Flush navel to lower lip)
	Governing Meridian	(Flush tailbone to upper lip)

Is there any reason I should not work with this person? ___yes ___no

Can we defuse this issue gently? ___yes ___no

Emotional Stress Statement (Chap. 5-36)

"I want and trust my ability to:_____"

"I do not want and do not trust my ability to:_____"

Stages of Stress (Chap. 2-2)

❐ None ❐ 1-glazed ❐ 2-one white ❐ 3-two whites ❐ 4-enlarged pupils.

Behavioral Barometer (Conscious, Subconscious, Body): (Addendum)

Key Subheading_____/_____

THE FULL STORY

Conscious	right_____	left_____
Subconscious	right_____	left_____
Body	right_____	left_____

Neg. Emot. Charge _____% (Chap. 5-1) Pos. Emot. Charge _____% (TOT*)

Permission to Age Recess ___yes ___no (Chap. 7-1)

Age Recess: to age of cause or best understanding: Age:___NEC:___% PEC___%

Barometer at this age:_____/_____

Defuse at this age: Emotional Digital Frontal Occipital Holding (Chap.8/18-21) or Body Scan Chap. 8/23 Check for clear Barometer and 0% NEC and 100% PEC.

INFUSE (Page 66 Tools of the Trade). Anchor as you return to Present Time.

Permission to Age Progress ___yes ___no (pg. 82-3 Tools of the Trade)

Age:_____ NEC:____% PEC:____%

Barometer at this age:_____/_____

DEFUSE with Frontal Occipital Holding and Sense Input. Check for clear Barometer and 0% NEC and 100% PEC. **RETURN TO PRESENT TIME.**

POST CHECK Stress Statement and 0% NEC on session itself.

BALANCE IS COMPLETE. CONGRATULATIONS!

BASIC ONE BRAIN - Balance 2

SET-UP MUSCLES - test contraction and extension

Chap. 3-16	*Clear Circuit muscles*	*(correct blocking)*
Chap. 4-3	*Overload*	*(Rub K-27's and hold navel)*
Chap. 4-7	*Central Meridian*	*(Flush navel to lower lip)*
	Governing Meridian	*(Flush tailbone to upper lip)*

Is there any reason I should not work with this person? ___yes ___no

Can we defuse this issue gently? ___yes ___no

Emotional Stress Statement (Chap. 5-36)

*"I want and trust my ability to:*_____*"*

*"I do not want and do not trust my ability to:*_____*"*

Stages of Stress (Chap. 2-2)

❒ None ❒ 1-glazed ❒ 2-one white ❒ 3-two whites ❒ 4-enlarged pupils.

Behavioral Barometer (Conscious, Subconscious, Body): (Addendum)

Key Subheading_____/_____

THE FULL STORY

Conscious	*right*_____	*left*_____	
Subconscious	*right*_____	*left*_____	
Body	*right*_____	*left*_____	

Neg. Emot. Charge _____% (Chap. 5-1) Pos. Emot. Charge _____% (TOT*)

ASSESSMENT

Chap. 5-1 **SET STANDARDS (Neg. Emotional Charge 1-100%)**

    *By Others*_____%

    *For Others*_____%

    *For Self*_____%

Chap. 5-30 **TRANSVERSE FLOW**_____

Chap. 5-24 **CROSS PATTERNING**

    *Cross pattern (should hold strong)*_____

    *Ipsilateral pattern (should not hold strong)*_____

    *Look at X (should hold strong)*_____

    *Look at II (should not hold strong)*_____

Chap. 5-32 **NUTRITION/GENETIC** *(touch glabella)*_____

Continued

Balance 2 - continued

DIGITALS IN PRESENT TIME: (check & correct if necessary - Electrical, Emotional and Nutritional)

PERMISSION TO AGE RECESS _____ (Chap. 7-1)

AGE RECESS: To age of cause or best understanding:

      AGE:_____ NEC: _____% PEC: _____%

BAROMETER AT THIS AGE:_____

DEFUSE AT THIS AGE: (check & correct Elec., Emot. & Nutrit. digitals

      Correction:_____ 2nd Correction:_____, etc.

Check for clear Barometer and 0% NEC and 100% PEC. If not age of cause, return to present time, check digitals, and then age recess again. If this was the age of cause:

INFUSE (page 66 Tools of the Trade). ANCHOR AS YOU RETURN TO P.T.

PERMISSION TO AGE PROGRESS ___yes ___no (Pg. 82-3 Tools)

      AGE:_____ NEC: _____% PEC:_____%

      BAROMETER AT THIS AGE: _____/_____

DEFUSE with Frontal Occipital Holding and Sense Input. Check for clear Barometer and 0% NEC and 100% PEC. RETURN TO PRESENT TIME

CHECK ISSUE AND ASSESSMENT OUTS PLUS 0% NEC ON SESSION.

BALANCE IS COMPLETE. CONGRATULATIONS!

BASIC ONE BRAIN - Balance 3

SET-UP MUSCLES - test contraction and extension

Chap. 3-16	Clear Circuit muscles	(correct blocking)
Chap. 4-3	Overload	(Rub K-27's and hold navel)
Chap. 4-7	Central Meridian	(Flush navel to lower lip)
	Governing Meridian	(Flush tailbone to upper lip)

Is there any reason I should not work with this person? ___yes ___no

Can we defuse this issue gently? ___yes ___no

Emotional Stress Statement (Chap. 5-36)

"I want and trust my ability to:_____"

"I do not want and do not trust my ability to:_____"

Stages of Stress (Chap. 2-2)

❏ None ❏ 1-glazed ❏ 2-one white ❏ 3-two whites ❏ 4-enlarged pupils.

Behavioral Barometer (Conscious, Subconscious, Body): (Addendum)

Key Subheading_____/_____

THE FULL STORY

Conscious	right_____	left_____
Subconscious	right_____	left_____
Body	right_____	left_____

Neg. Emot. Charge _____% (Chap. 5-1) Pos. Emot. Charge _____% (TOT*)

ASSESSMENT: Mark if not appropriate

Chap. 5-1 **SHORT CIRCUIT EYES:**

Eyes Open (left - right - up - down - midline)

Eyes Closed (left - right - up - down - midline)

Eyes Open (near - arm's length - far)

Eyes back and forth 20 times.

Chap. 15-16 **SHORT CIRCUIT EARS**

Turn head and listen to voice (left - right - midline)

Chap. 5-28 **HYOID** (gently move adam's apple)

Chap. 5-34 **CIA** (tap and hold behind dominant ear)

DIGITALS IN PRESENT TIME:

Check & Correct (Elect., Emot., Nutrit., Struct.)

Continued

PERMISSION TO AGE RECESS _____ Chap. 7 - 1

AGE RECESS: To age of cause or best understanding:

      AGE:_____ NEC:_____% PEC:_____%

BAROMETER AT THIS AGE:_____/_____

DEFUSE AT THIS AGE:

      Check & Correct (Elect., Emot., Nutrit., Struct.)

Correction_____ 2nd Correction? _____, etc.

Check for clear Barometer and 0% NEC and 100% PEC. If not age of cause, return to present time, check digitals, and then age recess again. If this is age of cause, correct to 0% and **INFUSE** (Pg. 66 Tools of the Trade).

ANCHOR AS YOU RETURN TO PRESENT TIME.

PERMISSION TO AGE PROGRESS _____ (Pg. 82-3 Tools of the Trade)

      AGE:_____ NEC_____% PEC_____%

BAROMETER AT THIS AGE:_____/_____

DEFUSE Then visualize how you would like your life to be at this time.

RETURN TO PRESENT TIME.

CHECK ISSUE AND ASSESSMENT OUT PLUS 0% NEC ON SESSION.

BALANCE IS COMPLETE. CONGRATULATIONS!

BASIC ONE BRAIN - Balance 4

SET-UP MUSCLES - test contraction and extension

Chap. 3-16	*Clear Circuit muscles*	*(correct blocking)*
Chap. 4-3	*Overload*	*(Rub K-27's and hold navel)*
Chap. 4-7	*Central Meridian*	*(Flush navel to lower lip)*
	Governing Meridian	*(Flush tailbone to upper lip)*

Is there any reason I should not work with this person? ___yes ___no

Can we defuse this issue gently? ___yes ___no

Emotional Stress Statement (Chap. 5-36)

"I want and trust my ability to:_____"

"I do not want and do not trust my ability to:_____"

Stages of Stress (Chap. 2-2)

❐ None ❐ 1-glazed ❐ 2-one white ❐ 3-two whites ❐ 4-enlarged pupils.

Behavioral Barometer (Conscious, Subconscious, Body): (Addendum)

Key Subheading_____/_____

THE FULL STORY

Conscious	*right_____*	*left_____*
Subconscious	*right_____*	*left_____*
Body	*right_____*	*left_____*

Neg. Emot. Charge _____% (Chap. 5-1) Pos. Emot. Charge _____% (TOT*)

ASSESSMENT: Mark if not appropriate

Chap. 5-5 **READING PERCEPTION** (read while testing)

    Forward

    Backward (one word at a time)

    Silently

    Comprehension (what did you just read?)

Chap. 5-6   *Alphabet*

Chap. 5-7   *Numbers 0-10*

Chap. 5-8 **CROSSING THE MIDLINE** (write sentence and test)

    L - Midline -R (test in contraction)   L-Midline-R (test in extension)

Chap. 5-19 **FIXATION TEST** (look at black paper)

Continued

ALL DIGITALS IN PRESENT TIME: Check & Correct if necessary

PERMISSION TO AGE RECESS ___yes ___no Chap. 7-1

AGE RECESS: to age of cause or best understanding

        AGE:____ NEC____% PEC____%

BAROMETER AT THIS AGE:_____/_____

DEFUSE AT THIS AGE: Check & Correct all digitals

Correction:_____ 2nd Correction?_____, etc.

Check for clear Barometer and 0% NEC and 100% PEC. If not age of cause, return to present time, check digitals, and then age recess again. If this was the age of cause:

INFUSE (Page 66 Tools of the Trade). Anchor as you return to Present Time.

Permission to Age Progress ___*yes* ___*no (pg. 82-3 Tools of the Trade)*

        Age:_____ NEC:____% PEC:____%

Barometer at this age:_____/_____

DEFUSE *with Frontal Occipital Holding and Sense Input. Check for clear Barometer and 0% NEC and 100% PEC.* **RETURN TO PRESENT TIME.**

POST CHECK Stress Statement and 0% NEC on session itself.

BALANCE IS COMPLETE. CONGRATULATIONS!

BASIC ONE BRAIN - Balance 5

SET-UP MUSCLES - test contraction and extension

Chap. 3-16	*Clear Circuit muscles*	*(correct blocking)*
Chap. 4-3	*Overload*	*(Rub K-27's and hold navel)*
Chap. 4-7	*Central Meridian*	*(Flush navel to lower lip)*
	Governing Meridian	*(Flush tailbone to upper lip)*

Is there any reason I should not work with this person? ___yes ___no

Can we defuse this issue gently? ___yes ___no

Emotional Stress Statement (Chap. 5-36)

"I want and trust my ability to:_____"

"I do not want and do not trust my ability to:_____"

Stages of Stress (Chap. 2-2)

❐ None ❐ 1-glazed ❐ 2-one white ❐ 3-two whites ❐ 4-enlarged pupils.

Behavioral Barometer (Conscious, Subconscious, Body): (Addendum)

Key Subheading_____/_____

THE FULL STORY

Conscious	*right_____*	*left_____*
Subconscious	*right_____*	*left_____*
Body	*right_____*	*left_____*

Neg. Emot. Charge _____% (Chap. 5-1) Pos. Emot. Charge _____% (TOT*)

DO BASIC ONE BRAIN EXAMINATION FOR ASSESSMENT
BEGIN CORRECTION

ALL DIGITALS IN PRESENT TIME: Check & Correct if necessary

PERMISSION TO AGE RECESS ___yes ___no Chap. 7-1

Permission *to Age Recess ___yes ___no (Chap. 7-1)*

Age Recess: *to age of cause or best understanding: Age:___NEC:___% PEC___%*

Barometer at this age:_____/_____

Defuse at this age: Check & Correct all digitals

Correction:_____ 2nd Correction? _____

Check for clear Barometer and 0% NEC and 100% PEC. If not age of cause, return to present time, check digitals, and then age recess again. If this is age of cause:

INFUSE *(Page 66 *Tools of the Trade). Anchor as you return to Present Time.*

Continued

Continued - Balance 5

Permission to Age Progress ___*yes* ___*no (pg. 82-3 Tools of the Trade)*
   Age:_____ **NEC:**_____% **PEC:**_____%
Barometer at this age:_____/_____
DEFUSE *with Frontal Occipital Holding and Sense Input. Check for clear*
Barometer and 0% NEC and 100% PEC. **RETURN TO PRESENT TIME.**

___

POST CHECK Stress Statement and 0% NEC on session itself.

BALANCE IS COMPLETE. CONGRATULATIONS!

Name _____   Date _____

BEHAVIORAL EVALUATION SHEET

Check if present <u>now</u>. Check TWICE if especially evident.
( ) indicates condition after correction. (S) same; (F) fair;
(G) good; (E) excellent; (N) not evident now.

__ Accident prone (   )
__ Allergies (   )
__ Bites nails (   )
__ Clumsy (   )
__ Conservative (   )
__ Constipated (   )
__ Daydreams (   )
__ Defiant/hard to discipline (   )
__ Difficulty budgeting time (   )
__ Difficulty concentrating (   )
__ Difficulty following directions (   )
__ Difficulty giving directions (   )
__ Difficulty making decisions (   )
__ Difficulty telling time (   )
__ Disturbing to others (   )
__ Does not handle stress (   )
__ Excitable (   )
__ Fights (   )
__ Has nightmares (   )
__ Headaches (   )
__ Immature for age (   )
__ Impatient (   )

__ Impulsive (   )
__ Lacks confidence (   )
__ Leaves projects incomplete (   )
__ Letter or number reversals (   )
__ Lies (   )
__ Moody (   )
__ Over-active (   )
__ Poor eye/hand coordination (   )
__ Poor handwriting (   )
__ Poor reading comprehension (   )
__ Reckless (   )
__ Restless/fidgety (   )
__ Rests head on arm when writing (   )
__ Rubs eyes a lot (   )
__ Sensitive (   )
__ Slow in completing work (   )
__ Stops in middle of game (   )
__ Talks too much (   )
__ Teaser (   )
__ Unpopular (   )
__ Unpredictable (   )
__ Wets bed (   )

DYSLEXIC CORRECTION AND BEHAVIORAL CHANGES

You may find the above Behavioral Evaluation a real plus in
your work with ONE BRAIN corrections. We certainly have
and we use it with many clients, young and older, PRIOR to
defusing so-called "learning dysfunctions and disabilities." As
you've seen, the Evaluation covers a lot of ground. We
designed it to identify troublesome behaviors OTHER than
dyslexic perception so that all parties involved in "the
problem" can appreciate positive changes.

Here's why the Behavioral Evaluation makes such a contribution.

Our response to stressors, whether fight or flight, manifests in our posture, usual gestures and other physical signals. For instance, if we met continued resistance to our behavior as we grew up - and that resistance happens again and again - we may distort our physical habits to accommodate that stressor. That habit might make us develop a tilt to the head, inclining it away from things we don't want to hear or see. Or we might choose not to perceive such stressors at all.

In such a manner, we may continually block vision in one eye so that eventually, after years of repeating this perceptual bad habit, we go "blind" in one eye or deaf in one ear for no clinically identifiable cause. Difficult as it is for many to believe that much deafness and loss of vision results from emotionally-based perceptual bad habits, our experience tells us it's true. We wanted to survive the pressure, and we did - but at what a cost!

Perception of sight and sound depends as much on what we are PREPARED TO PERCEIVE as on our organs of perception. The eyes are only light receptors for the brain; the ears are only sound receptors. We don't see or hear exact replications of what exists "out there." Our visual/audio perception is affected by memory, judgment, CHOICE and previous experience.

Remember, the brain listens to ALL messages from the senses before it identifies an image, sound, thought or reaches a conclusion. 20% of the information from the retina never reaches visual cortex to be used for sight. It travels to other brain centers for integration with more data about the body's orientation, position in space, and what's heard at the moment of visual perception. (Ditto for the processing of what we hear; the sound transfer includes the same integrated inter-mesh of sense/body information.)

The way we think affects our vision, and our vision affects the way we think and the way we think has to do with our responses to our environment, and feedback from these responses have to do with our self-esteem. So in working in one area such as reading or comprehension, we're working with ALL areas of an individual's life. **Because of this, ONE BRAIN corrections usually result in positive behavioral changes as well as perceptual improvement.**

And being aware that changes in perception have taken place, we need to realize that we're no longer dealing with "the same person" now. Free of a dyslexic blind spot, the person has become a growing, changing individual. We need to see that person with new eyes and tune into the behavioral changes that go hand in hand with perceptual improvement. What's more, we need to verbally identify and validate them, since that helps the person appreciate the significance of the changes taking place.

Our different response to these positive changes of behavior permits the individual to "see" them, too, and benefit from them all the more. **So be aware of positive changes and respond differently to the behavioral changes you observe.**

1985 GRANT RESULTS

CLASSROOM: TEACHER INSTRUCTIONAL IMPROVEMENT PROGRAM

Title of Project: DEFUSING DYSLEXIA

School: SIERRA VISTA JUNIOR HIGH SCHOOL

Applicant: LEE WASSERWALD
Special Education Teacher

Consultant: Three In One Concepts
2001 W. Magnolia Blvd.
Burbank, CA 91506
818-841-4786

Preface:
Eleven Special Education Students, three to seven years behind their grade level, participated in the program. These students have been in Special Education for several years and most display attitudes towards school ranging from boredom to disgust.

Specific Objectives for the Program:
To determine, through the Defusing Dyslexia Project, positive effects in learning, motivation, and academic performance. Also if students' attitudes towards school and learning, as well as behavior, would improve.

Testing Procedure:
Academic pre and post testing which involved such tests as the Wrat spelling, reading and math; the Nelson paragraph comprehension test; parental observations of any changes in their child (behavioral, academic or affective); oral reading comparison (recorded on tape), written language comparison and information retention and comprehension.

Timeline:
  Eight weeks. Consultant to work with the students each Monday of every week.

Change accomplished/not accomplished:
  Defining "significant" as anything above a year's growth, eight of the eleven students showed significant growth in one or six of the testing areas. The growth ranged from an increase of 1.2 years in one student to 3.2 in another. Three of the students showed no significant change. No student tested a negative significant change.

Parent Comments:
  Of the eleven responses, seven were extremely positive and one slightly positive in noting changes in the children. Even more impressive was the pattern of similar words used in the letters, i.e., "calmer, less complaining, more responsible, more assured and self-confident."

  "Calmest (we) have seen her. More agreeable, responsible and confident."

  "Less complaining. Less anger. Less need for help on homework. More motivated and determined to finish projects."

  "No significant change."

  "Calmer, slightly more responsible."

  "Writes more complicated answers without complaining. Handles schoolwork more easily. Reading and spelling easier for him. Math noticeably improved."

  "More patience, more respect for others, more responsible with a greater self-concept."

"Calmer, more peaceful."

"More successful with schoolwork. Development of a sense of humor. More responsible and helpful. More assured with himself."

"No significant change."

"Improved attitudes in reading, math, school and general schoolwork. Improved attitudes in self-confidence."

Student comments:

Student, age 14, male said thoughts were clearer. Felt less worried, much smarter and more even-tempered.

Student, age 15, male said some feeling (sensation) returned to an injured left hand. Felt perceptual reach for objects better.

Student, age 13, male said he was reading more.

Teacher Comments:

Of the six categories, 2 students improved significantly in one category, 4 students in two divisions, one student in three aspects, one person in four categories and two students in five categories and one in all six.

From another perspective, 73% of the students improved significantly in three divisions, 50% in one, and 27% in two others. Furthermore, the parental comments were extremely impressive. The similarity of words and perceptions set a pattern indicative of positive change.

The project was an outstanding success. The corrections appeared to lessen or remove some blockages to the learning process so that the tasks became more understandable and easier. In consideration of this, the evaluator will consider asking for a continuation of the grant with some minor changes in the timetable and testing.

Note: Second grant was approved for 1986.

BIBLIOGRAPHY

Eckstein, G., The Body Has A Head, Harper & Row, 1969

Esch, D. & Lepley, M., Musculoskeletal Function, U of Minnesota Press, 1974

Fried, L.A., Anatomy of the Head, Neck, Face and Jaws, Lea & Febiger, 1980

Guyton, A.C., Physiology of the Human Body, W. B. Saunders Co, 1979

Kavner, R. S. & Dusky, L., Total Vision, A. & W. Publishers, Inc, 1978

Kendall, F.P. & McCreary, E.K., Muscles Testing and Function, Waverly Press, Inc., 1983

Malstrom, S. & Myer, M., Own Your Own Body, Bell Press, 1977

Penfield, W. & Roberts, L., Speech and Brain-Mechanisms, Atheneum, 1966

Rasch, P.J., & Burke, R. K., Kinesiology and applied Anatomy, Lea & Febiger, 1978

Restak, R.M., The Brain the Last Frontier, Warner Books, 1979

Schaeffer (Editor), Morris Human Anatomy, Blakiston Co., 1946

Stokes, G. & Marks, M., Dr. Sheldon Deal's Chiropractic Assistants and Doctors Basic AK Workshop Manual, Touch for Health, 1983

Stokes, G. & Whiteside, D., Structural Neurology, Three In One concepts, 1985

Stokes, G. & Whiteside, D., Under the Code, Three In One Concepts, 1985

The Human Body Series, U. S. News Books, 1985

Thie, J., Touch For Health, DeVorss Co, 1973

Thompson, C.W., Manual of Structural Kinesiology, C. V. Mosby Co., 1985

Walther, D.S., Applied Kinesiology, Systems D.C., 1976

Wooldridge, D. E., The Machinery of the Brain, McGraw-Hill, Inc., 1963

Zeig, J. K., Ericksonian Approaches to Hypnosis and Psychotherapy, Brunner/Mazel, Publishers, 1982

INDEX

ABOUT THE AUTHORS

GORDON STOKES

The president of Three In One, Gordon's unique overview of body/brain integration puts him in the vanguard of the self-health maintenance movement. He has presented our programs throughout the English-speaking world as well as in Norway, Holland, Germany, Denmark - and Brazil. His incredible knowledge of Applied Kinesiology, acupressure and neurological circuitry blends with a background in behavioral genetics, psychodrama and role-play training. The result: programs as rich in communication skills as body-work specifics. Gordon's kind and gentle style facilitates the learning process with amazing ease. A master teacher, he creates interest, assurance and attunement in all who study with him.

DANIEL WHITESIDE

Internationally known for his pioneering work in behavioral genetics, Daniel has guested on numerous radio and television programs as well as appearing in several award-winning educational film/video series. He authors all our publications in collaboration with Gordon's original research in addition to having written two published novels and the best-selling HOW TO WIN OVER YOURSELF - an introduction to behavioral genetics. A brilliant, witty man, his incredible knowledge of literature, archeology, history, neurological brain function, art, music and metaphysics characterizes Three In One's programs. As a presenter he blends whimsy and wisdom with the style of attuned multi-dimensional awareness.

Publications from
THREE IN ONE CONCEPTS
written by
Gordon Stokes/Daniel Whiteside

ONE BRAIN
Dyslexic Learning Correction and Brain Integration

You can use the text for the Basic ONE BRAIN workshop to **identify and correct** the body-effects that lock-in learning disability. Help yourself, family, friends and clients greatly improve reading, comprehension, writing and math abilities. Also included: the best illustrated, simplest, information on how the brain works - and how you can make it work better.

ADVANCED ONE BRAIN
Dyslexia - The Emotional Cause

This text for the Advanced ONE BRAIN training focuses on how to **identify and correct** learning disability's negative **emotional cause.** It introduces the Behavioral Barometer and a whole battery of Emotional Stress Defusion techniques, as well as expanding on Digital Determination, the genetic impact of structure on food sensitivity and much more.

UNDER THE CODE

A whole new approach to people-skills, UNDER THE CODE shows you how to **identify and correct** your dyslexic **mis-perception of self and others.** It enables you to see at first glance another's deep, inner needs and attune to Being instead of reacting to personality - as well as giving you a unique formula to establish and maintain good communication.

LOUDER THAN WORDS

With this text for our second people-skills program, you can **identify and appreciate** the subconscious and body genetic programming behind any conscious clash of values or communication "out." It covers all 48 of the Structure-equals-Function factors and offers you the insight to bridge gaps in awareness that otherwise you wouldn't dream exist.

STRUCTURAL NEUROLOGY

Here we integrate and synthesize all previous information to **identify and release** Pain and Pain Behavior - with a special focus on defusing addiction, obsession and phobia. In addition, the text presents in-depth insight into the integrated neurology of structure: the Body and Muscle Circuits that relate to the release of chronic blocked energy.